5

Edexcel GCSE (9–1) History

Early Elizabethan England, 1558–88

Georgina Blair

Published by Pearson Education Limited, 80 Strand, London, WC2R ORL.

www.pearsonschoolsandfecolleges.co.uk

Copies of official specifications for all Pearson qualifications may be found on the website: qualifications.pearson.com

Produced by Out of House Publishing Solutions
Typeset by Newgen KnowledgeWorks Pvt. Ltd., Chennai, India

First published 2017

19 18 17
10 9 8 7 6 5 4 3 2 1

British Library Cataloguing in Publication Data
A catalogue record for this book is available from the British Library

ISBN 978 0 435 18946 4

Printed in Slovakia by Neografia

Note from the publisher
Pearson has robust editorial processes, including answer and fact checks, to ensure the accuracy of the content in this publication, and every effort is made to ensure this publication is free of errors. We are, however, only human, and occasionally errors do occur. Pearson is not liable for any misunderstandings that arise as a result of errors in this publication, but it is our priority to ensure that the content is accurate. If you spot an error, please do contact us at resourcescorrections@pearson.com so we can make sure it is corrected.

Contents

1 Selecting and deploying your own knowledge

This unit will help you to learn how you can decide what information to select for questions which rely on your own historical knowledge. The skills you will build are how to:

- choose historical knowledge based on what the question is asking you
- decide how much of your own historical knowledge you need to include in an answer
- use your own historical knowledge effectively.

In the exam, you will be asked to tackle questions such as the one below. This unit will prepare you to write your own response to this question:

Exam-style question

Describe **two** key features of local government in Elizabethan England. **(4 marks)**

There are three types of question you will have to answer in your GCSE exam:

(a) describe two key features of something

(b) explain why something happened

(c) decide how far you agree with something.

You don't need to write about everything you know on a question, but you do need to be able to decide what is important to include in your answer. You also need to be able to develop your own point of view for (c) type questions. Whatever the question, stronger answers are supported by well-chosen historical evidence.

The three key questions in the **skills boosts** will help you to decide what historical knowledge you need when you are answering Paper 2 history questions.

How do I identify a relevant key feature from my own knowledge?

2 **How do I back up my points with relevant detail?**

How do I use my historical knowledge to write effectively?

On the next page are another exam-style question and a student answer.

Get started

What do you think about if someone mentions Tudor England?

- Powerful monarchs?
- Half-timbered houses?
- Heads being cut off?
- People wearing ruffs and men wearing tights?

These are all 'typical' or characteristic of Tudor England. They are all **key features** of Tudor England.

Key features are typical, clearly recognisable characteristics about a person, place or era in history.

Exam-style question

Describe **two** key features of the problems facing Elizabeth when she became queen in 1558. **(4 marks)**

Elizabeth I became queen of England in 1558 after the death of her sister, Mary I. As Mary I had had no children, Elizabeth was next in line although she was a woman. One key feature of the problems Elizabeth I faced on becoming queen was her gender. In Elizabethan society it was usual for men to be in positions of authority and she was only England's second queen. Mary is sometimes known as 'Bloody Mary' because she burned over 300 Protestants.

1. a. Highlight the key feature the student has chosen to write about.
   b. Circle (A) the supporting detail the student has chosen to use.
   c. Cross out ~~cat~~ anything that is not necessary to answer the exam-style question.

The student answer uses two sentences to describe **one** key feature of the problems faced by Elizabeth I when she became queen. The student has made notes on the second key feature they could write about.

2. a. Tick three statements that could be used to build a description of **one** other key feature.

A	*There was a dispute about whether Elizabeth was legitimate.*	☐
B	*Mary, Queen of Scots had a strong claim to the English throne and there was no question of her legitimacy.*	☐
C	*Scotland and France were both traditional enemies of England and had an ancient friendship known as the Auld Alliance.*	☐
D	*Many Catholics did not accept Henry VIII's marriage to Elizabeth's mother, Anne Boleyn.*	☐
E	*Henry VIII had once declared her illegitimate.*	☐
F	*Mary, Queen of Scots had been married to the heir to the French throne.*	☐

   b. Write which feature you have identified.

Remember all you need to answer this question are two key features and supporting detail for each one.

....

....

....

Elizabethan society

This unit uses the theme of Elizabethan society to build your skills in selecting and deploying your own knowledge. If you need to review your knowledge of this theme, work through these pages.

① Write the word, beginning with H, that best describes the structure of Elizabethan society.

....

② Fill in the gaps in the diagrams using the words listed below the pyramids.

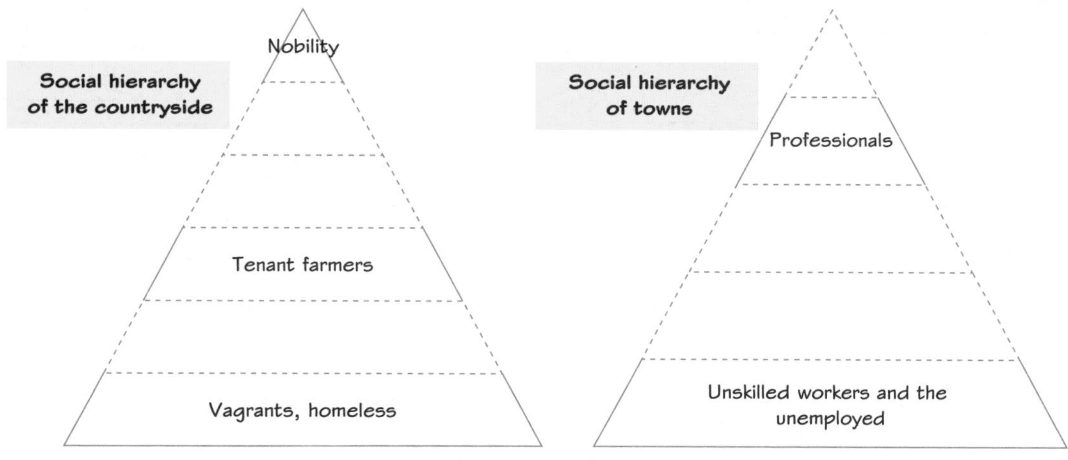

gentry | landless, labouring poor | merchants | skilled craftsmen | business owners | yeomen

③ Draw lines linking the part of the government on the left to the correct description on the right (there may be more than one description to link to each part of the government).

part of government	description
A Court	a approximately 19 advisers who met at least three times a week
B Privy Council	b could offer advice and pass laws
C Parliament	c entertained and advised the monarch
D Lords Lieutenant	d granted the monarch extraordinary taxation
E Justices of the Peace (JPs)	e heard serious county court cases every three months
	f in charge of raising and training county militia
	g kept law and order locally
	h made up of leading courtiers and government advisers
	i public display of monarch's wealth and power
	j saw all social and economic policies were carried out locally

④ Write two examples of the monarch's powers.

....

....

5 Draw lines linking the questions and answers.

A Which two things were part of parliament's role?	a Raising special taxes called subsidies
B Which three things were problems for Elizabeth I?	b Mary, Queen of Scots
C Who was Elizabeth I's cousin?	c Mary I
D Who was Elizabeth I's sister?	d The question of her legitimacy
E Which two are sources of Crown finance?	e Providing an heir to the throne
F Which two things linked Scotland to France?	f Rents from Crown lands
	g Advising the monarch
	h The Auld Alliance

6 Read the following statements about Elizabethan history and tick to say if they are true or false.

		true	false
a	Elizabeth I wanted to marry and produce an heir as soon as possible.		
b	Elizabeth I was Protestant but Mary, Queen of Scots was Catholic.		
c	England had just taken possession of the French town of Calais.		
d	The court had two purposes: it was a public display of the monarch's wealth and power; and it was to entertain the monarch.		
e	Sir William Cecil was Elizabeth I's Prime Minister.		
f	Mary, Queen of Scots became queen of France in 1559.		
g	Mary, Queen of Scots was queen of Scotland.		
h	Elizabeth I could be very frustrating as she took so long to make up her mind.		

7 a Circle which of the following were ways the monarch could raise money.

i fines from people convicted of crimes

ii loans

iii subsidies agreed by parliament

iv customs duties

b Circle which of the facts below applied to the Privy Council.

i oversaw law and order and England's security

ii voted on laws

iii was appointed by the monarch

iv was part of local government

c Circle which of the following were powers of the monarch.

i giving grants of land, money and jobs

ii calling and dismissing parliament

iii giving rulings in some legal cases

iv declaring war and making peace

How do I identify a relevant key feature from my own knowledge?

When it comes to finding what you need for a key features question, there are some guidelines that can help you. This skills boost will help you to use these guidelines.

Elizabeth I became queen on 17 November 1558. This is a fact. It might be important, but is not a key feature. Elizabeth I had red hair. This is also a fact. She had red hair **for a long time**. It is a **key feature** of Elizabeth I's appearance that she had red hair.

During Elizabeth's reign, Drake circumnavigated the globe 1577–1580. It is a fact. It is one event. It is, however, one of many voyages of exploration that took place. There are **lots of examples** of voyages of exploration during Elizabeth I's reign. It is exploration that is a **key feature** of Elizabeth's reign.

1. Tick the key features of Elizabethan England from the list below.

Remember: relevant key features will be characteristic or typical of Elizabethan England – not one-off events. This means things that were common, or happened often or for long periods of time.

A The exploration of America ☐

B The growth of grammar schools ☐

C The founding of Jesus College, Oxford ☐

D Elizabeth I catching smallpox in 1562 ☐

E Relations with Spain being poor ☐

F Cuthbert Mayne being executed in 1577 ☐

2. Highlight at least **two** key features of Elizabeth I's reign from this student answer.

Throughout Elizabeth's reign there was an increase in poverty and her government developed new ways of dealing with the poor. Elizabeth was often under threat from Catholic plots, such as Ridolfi in 1572, Throckmorton in 1583 and Babington in 1586. These all involved Mary, Queen of Scots, who was a serious problem for Elizabeth from when she arrived in England in 1568 until her execution in 1587. Elizabeth is best known for the defeat of the Spanish Armada. Her heir was James VI of Scotland, who became king when she died in 1603.

2 How do I back up my points with relevant detail?

It is important to support the points you make, otherwise you are simply making assertions or writing descriptions. This skills boost will help you to do this.

Assertions make **weak** history. Assertions are statements with no support.

Supporting detail makes for **strong** history. Statements with support make a well-supported point.

1. Highlight which of the following are assertions:

   A Elizabeth I was a strong monarch because she was determined, intelligent and highly educated.

   B Tudor monarchs were not as powerful as is often thought.

   C Mary I made an unpopular marriage and burned 300 Protestants, so she was not well-liked.

   D A key feature of the Elizabethan Parliament was that it was very weak.

   E A key feature of Elizabeth I's reign was that Philip II wanted to get rid of her.

   F A key feature of Elizabeth I's life was danger, such as being sent to the Tower in 1554 or the threats to her life in 1583 and 1586.

The following questions can help you decide what factual support to use.

? Is it relevant to the question?

? Is there more than one example of it? For instance, Elizabeth faced many plots.

? Are there specific details you could use, such as: facts, figures and examples?

2. a A key feature of Elizabeth I's reign was that Philip II wanted to get rid of her. Highlight two of the following which would make good supporting detail for this key feature.

   A Philip II thought that Elizabeth I was a threat to him.

   B Philip II encouraged the Ridolfi, Throckmorton and Babington plots against Elizabeth I.

   C Philip II did not like Protestants.

   D Philip II did not like Elizabeth I.

   E Elizabeth I supported the Dutch rebels against Spain in the Netherlands.

   b Write the reasons why you have chosen these two below:

Supporting detail 1:

I chose .... *because* ....

....

Supporting detail 2:

I chose .... *because* ....

....

3 How do I use my historical knowledge to write effectively?

To answer a knowledge-based question you need to back up what your key points are and support them with details. This skills boost will help you to practise these skills.

Look at the exam-style question below and the extract of a student's answer to it.

Exam-style question

Describe **two** key features of Elizabethan society. **(4 marks)**

One key feature of Elizabethan society was that it was a hierarchy. Your place in it depended on how much land you had and how wealthy you were. For example, in the countryside, the nobility were at the top of society and vagrants were at the bottom.

1. Look at the extract above.
   - a Highlight the key feature that has been chosen.
   - b Circle where the key feature has been backed up with supporting detail.
   - c Underline the words that show that the student has focused on the question.

2. Pick a key feature of Elizabethan society from the list below and write the second part of the answer for this question.
   - Town society was based on wealth and jobs.
   - Elizabethan society was very unequal.
   - In Elizabethan town society, skilled craftsmen belonged to guilds.

3. Annotate your answer.
   - a Highlight the key feature.
   - b Circle the supporting detail.
   - c Underline the words to show that you have focused on the question.

Remember to support your statements with relevant detail.

Sample response

The skill of selecting and deploying your own knowledge is important for all the questions you might be asked in your history GCSE. Apply what you have learned to the student response below.

Exam-style question

Describe **two** features of the role of the monarch in Elizabethan England. **(4 marks)**

Look at this student's response to the exam-style question above.

Elizabeth I was 25 when she came to the throne. It was thought unnatural for a woman to have authority. One important feature was that, as queen, she could rule in some legal cases such as when people appealed directly to her or the law was unclear. Not everyone agreed that Elizabeth should be queen as not everyone believed that Henry VIII could divorce Catherine of Aragon to marry Anne Boleyn. As queen, Elizabeth had a lot of power because monarchs in those days made all the important decisions.

1. Answer the three questions about this response in the table below by putting a tick in the box on the right (Yes, Partly or No) that you think most appropriate.

Think about ...	Yes	Partly	No
Does the response answer the question?			
Is there any description that doesn't show a key feature of the monarch in Elizabethan England?			
Is the supporting detail strong? Is it precise and relevant?			

2. Highlight one sentence in the student response that satisfies all the questions from the table above.

3. Rewrite the last sentence so that it gives a strong, supported feature of the monarch in Elizabethan England. Remember to give examples of important decisions made to show that the monarch had a lot of power.

Your turn!

Now it's your turn to try to answer an exam-style question.

Exam-style question

Describe **two** key features of local government in Elizabethan England. **(4 marks)**

1 a Here is some research that a student carried out on the question above. Tick the information you think is most useful.

- *2 key parts of local government = lords lieutenant and JPs*
- *Each county had a Lord Lieutenant – nobility – were often on Privy Council too*
- *JPs = popular job and gave people status*
- *JPs = local landowners, they were unpaid and reported to Privy Council*
- *Lords Lieutenant:*
  - *raised and trained local militias*
  - *oversaw enforcement of government policies*
- *JPs:*
  - *heard serious court cases every 3 months*
  - *ensured all social and economic policies were carried out, e.g. collection of poor rates*

b Write an answer using the research you have selected.

Review your skills

Check up

Review your response to the exam-style question on page 9. Tick ✓ the column below to show how well you think you have done each of the following.

	Not quite ✓	Nearly there ✓	Got it! ✓
gave two different key features	☐	☐	☐
used strong supporting details about each key feature	☐	☐	☐
did not add unnecessary information	☐	☐	☐

Look over all of your work in this unit. Note down three things you have learned that you will apply when using your own knowledge in answering history questions in future.

1. ....

2. ....

3. ....

Need more practice?

You will need to practise what has been covered in this unit to answer all the other exam-style questions in this workbook. If you want to practise another 4-mark question, try this one on a separate piece of paper.

Exam-style question

Describe **two** key features of the threat posed by Mary, Queen of Scots to Elizabeth I. **(4 marks)**

How confident do you feel about each of these **skills**? Colour in the bars.

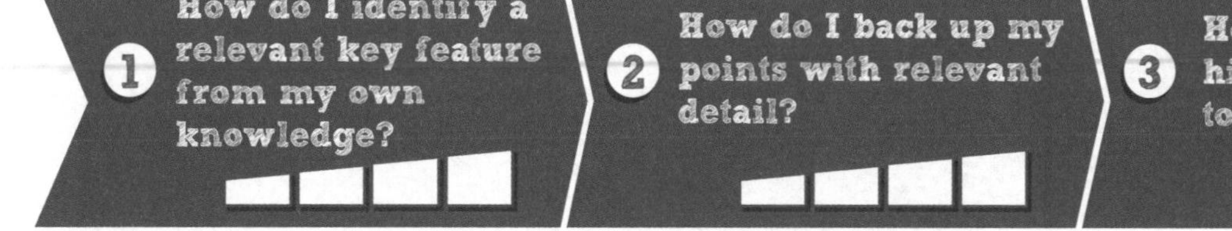

1 How do I identify a relevant key feature from my own knowledge?
2 How do I back up my points with relevant detail?
3 How do I use my historical knowledge to write effectively?

2 Answering relevantly

This unit will help you do what the question asks you to do. The skills you will build are to:

- understand what the question wants you to do
- check that what you are including is relevant
- plan to make sure you have covered the whole question.

In the exam, you will also be asked to tackle questions like the one below. This unit will prepare you to write your own response to this type of question.

Exam-style question

Explain why Elizabeth I faced opposition to her religious settlement in the years 1558–1569.

You may use the following in your answer:

- the vestments controversy
- the Revolt of the Northern Earls.

You **must** also include information of your own. **(12 marks)**

To answer relevantly you need to ask yourself these two questions:

? Am I doing what the question is asking me to do?

? Am I using the best information to answer the question?

The three key questions in the **skills boosts** will help you to make sure your answer is relevant.

1 **How do I know what the question wants me to do?**

2 **How do I know what information is relevant?**

3 **How do I know I have covered the whole question?**

Here is a student's plan to answer the exam-style question on page 11.

	Points to make	Evidence
Intro	*Religious settlement was Protestant but there was opposition from both Catholics and Protestants*	
Section 1	*Puritans – extreme Protestants, thought religious settlement too Catholic. Didn't like Catholic look / feel of churches*	*Examples of Puritan beliefs, e.g. no bishops; no decoration; no miracle in mass*
	Opposition sometimes very strong	*Crucifix controversy – Elizabeth I backed down*
Section 2	*Revolt of the Northern Earls 1569 opposed religious settlement; North of England Catholic*	*Catholic mass at Durham cathedral; third of nobles and lots of gentry in north = Catholic*
	Rebellion aim = restore Catholic religion	*Plot to put Mary, Queen of Scots on throne; she had strong claim so could be Catholic queen*
	Earls angry and jealous of Elizabeth I's favourites	*Robert Dudley, William Cecil*
	Many Catholics opposed religious settlement because of the pope	*Papal bull of excommunication 1570*
Conclusion	*Evidence shows opposition was from both Catholic and Protestants. Protestants thought the religious settlement too Catholic. Catholic opposition that led to the Northern Rebellion wanted Mary, Queen of Scots to become queen of England.*	

(1) Is there anything in the plan that is not relevant to the question? Cross (~~cat~~) it out.

(2) Annotate the plan with any additional information you think may be useful.

The Elizabethan religious settlement

This unit uses the theme of the Elizabethan religious settlement to build your skills in answering relevantly. If you need to review your knowledge of this theme, work through these pages.

1. Write the religion of:
   a. Elizabeth I

   b. the majority of her subjects.

2. Give two reasons why English Catholics might not accept Elizabeth I as their queen.
   1
   2

3. Sort the cities and counties into the table, according to how Catholic or Protestant they were.

Durham | Lancashire | Essex | London | Kent | Stafford

Mostly Catholic	Mostly Protestant

4. Give two key features of the Puritan religion.
   1
   2

5. Briefly describe what these three parts of the Elizabethan religious settlement did.

Act of Supremacy	
Act of Uniformity	
Royal Injunctions	

6. Outline the punishment in the Act of Uniformity for not attending church.

7 Tick which of the following were part of the role of the Church of England.

a Enforcing the religious settlement ☐
b Leading pilgrimages ☐
c Controlling what was preached ☐
d Running church courts ☐

8 Link each answer with its question.

A 1 shilling
B recusant
C 8,000
D 27

a What was the name for a Catholic who did not attend Church of England church services?
b How many English priests took the oath of supremacy to Elizabeth I?
c What was the fine for not going to church on a Sunday or holy day?
d How many English bishops refused to take the oath of supremacy to Elizabeth I?

9 Read these statements about visitations. Tick to say if these statements are true or false.

	true	false
a Visitations occurred to enforce the religious settlement.		
b The first visitations were in 1559.		
c 1,000 clergy were dismissed after the first visitations.		
d Visitations took place every ten years.		
e Visitations inspected licences of preachers, midwives, surgeons and teachers.		

10 Decide whether each of the following statements describes the crucifix or vestment controversy, or both, by writing 'C', 'V' or 'C+V' alongside each.

a This was about ornaments in churches. ☐
b 37 priests lost their positions after attending a clothing exhibition. ☐
c This was a protest from Protestants rather than Catholics. ☐
d Elizabeth I had to back down. ☐

11 In 1569, the Earls of Northumberland and Westmorland led a rebellion against Elizabeth I in the north of England. Complete the following table on the Revolt of the Northern Earls.

Causes of the rebellion	Outcome / consequences of the rebellion

How do I know what the question wants me to do?

To answer the question relevantly you need to understand what the question is asking you to do.

1. Here are some useful words for understanding a question's instructions. Draw a line between each word and its meaning.

A Describe	a A sensible conclusion weighing up what you think about something based on a range of evidence.
B Explain	b To make clear, or give a reason for, something.
C Judgement ('How far do you agree?')	c To show or illustrate something using words.

2. Look at these three types of exam-style question. Then complete the tasks below.

Exam-style question

Describe **two** features of the monarchy in Elizabethan England. **(4 marks)**

Exam-style question

Explain why Elizabeth I faced opposition to her religious settlement in the years 1558–1569.

You may use the following in your answer:

- the vestments controversy
- the Revolt of the Northern Earls.

You **must** also include information of your own. **(12 marks)**

Exam-style question

'The Elizabethan religious settlement largely resolved religious tensions in England.'
How far do you agree? Explain your answer.

You may use the following in your answer:

- the crucifix controversy
- the Revolt of the Northern Earls, 1569.

You **must** also include information of your own. **(16 marks)**

a. Circle the words that give instructions on how to answer the question.

b. Underline the parts of the topic you need to write about.

c. Highlight anything else you need to write about such as dates, specific events, people or features.

2 How do I know what information is relevant?

To help you decide relevant information to include in your answers, ask yourself these questions:
- What do I know about the issue in the question?
- Can I use it to help me explain the opposition to the religious settlement?
- Is there anything I could add to develop the explanation further?

Look again at this exam-style question you saw on page 15.

Exam-style question

Explain why Elizabeth I faced opposition to her religious settlement in the years 1558–1569.

You may use the following in your answer:
- the vestments controversy
- the Revolt of the Northern Earls.

You **must** also include information of your own. **(12 marks)**

The relevance test: If you are not sure whether something is relevant to the question, try this simple test. Put your evidence in a sentence. For example:

This piece of evidence shows a reason why there was opposition to the Elizabethan religious settlement because …

If you can't complete it, don't use it!

1. Some information on the Revolt of the Northern Earls is listed below. Tick ✓ the statements that would help you to explain why there was opposition to Elizabeth I's religious settlement.

 a. The earls involved were Roman Catholic. ☐
 b. The earls were angry at their loss of political power. ☐
 c. Robert Dudley told Elizabeth I of the plot. ☐
 d. The rebels heard mass at Durham Cathedral. ☐
 e. Jane Neville played an important role in the rebellion. ☐
 f. The new archbishop of Durham was very Protestant and very unpopular. ☐
 g. The majority of England's nobles, Catholic and Protestant, stayed loyal to Elizabeth I. ☐
 h. The north of England was very Catholic. ☐

2. a. You must also include information of your own in your answer. Put a cross ~~cat~~ beside the **two** options that would **not** be relevant to the question.

 i The Ridolfi plot 1571 ☐
 ii Mary, Queen of Scots ☐
 iii The papal bull of excommunication 1570 ☐
 iv The oath of supremacy ☐

 b. Explain why ✎ they would not be relevant.

....

....

....

3 How do I know I have covered the whole question?

Try making a quick checklist when you are planning your answer to a question. When you have finished, check your finished answer to make sure you have covered everything on the list.

Below is a checklist for the exam-style question on page 16.

Checklist	✓
Explain	
Vestments controversy	
Northern Rebellion	
Information of my own	

Words and phrases for explaining

because	one reason is	this shows
this meant that	for example	as a result
another reason why	this led to	

1. Read this extract from a student's answer to the exam-style question on page 16.

The north of England was very Catholic. One-third of the nobility were Catholic and many of the gentry were too. This meant that Elizabeth I's choice of a Protestant bishop of Durham was very unpopular. For example, the rebels held mass at Durham Cathedral during the rebellion. Elizabeth I sent an army to put down the Catholic rebellion and there were hundreds of executions. The rebellion showed that there was serious Catholic opposition to the Church becoming more Protestant.

Some clergy felt that it was wrong for a woman to lead the church. This led to opposition. Some clergy refused to take the oath of allegiance to the queen. Only one bishop took it in 1559. There was less opposition among the lower clergy. 8,000 from 10,000 parishes took the oath. Visitations of parishes around England were carried out by bishops every three to four years. They checked that clergy had taken the oath and were preaching along the lines of the religious settlement.

Tick ✓ the table below to show if the student explains why there was opposition to the Elizabethan religious settlement.

Which paragraph ...	Paragraph 1 ✓	Paragraph 2 ✓
includes relevant information about opposition?		
develops an explanation of why there was opposition?		

2. Tick ✓ the checklist at the top of the page to decide whether everything needed for a relevant answer is included in the extract. If not, what is missing? Write ✎ your answer below.

Sample response

Look at this exam-style question.

Exam-style question

Explain why Elizabeth I was able to successfully enforce her religious settlement in the years 1558–1569.

You may use the following in your answer:

- the Act of Supremacy
- visitations.

You **must** also include information of your own. **(12 marks)**

1. As you read the student's answer below to the exam-style question:
   - a underline where the student is using words and phrases that show explanation
   - b circle where the student has included relevant information about the prompts
   - c highlight in one colour where the student has included relevant information from their own knowledge
   - d highlight in another colour where the student has been irrelevant.

Elizabeth I was able to enforce her religious settlement because it gave the Church of England powers to make sure that the clergy were obeying it. Visitations were a good way of doing this. A visitation was an inspection and the first ones were in 1559. Some ended up with ornaments in churches being destroyed because they were thought to be too Catholic. This angered Elizabeth I. She liked crucifixes, for example, although when puritans disagreed she had to back down on having them in all the churches. Visitations also included making sure that the clergy had licences to preach. This helped Elizabeth I to enforce the religious settlement because anyone who wanted a licence had to preach her religious settlement. For example, they preached royal supremacy.

The Act of Supremacy was a way of enforcing the religious settlement because it said that everyone had to take an oath to Elizabeth I as leader of the Church of England.

Another way of enforcing the religious settlement was when Matthew Parker dealt with the vestments controversy. This is because he made it very clear what priests were expected to wear and those who refused lost their positions. This was another reason why Elizabeth I could enforce her religious settlement: priests who disobeyed knew they would lose their jobs.

2. Write feedback for this student. Give one strength and one weakness.
   - a Strength

   ....

   ....

   - b Weakness

   ....

   ....

Your turn!

1. Look at the part of the student's answer on page 18 that covers how the Act of Supremacy helped to enforce the religious settlement. You are now going to:

   a rewrite and improve that part of the answer

   b add a reason of your own why Elizabeth I was able to enforce the religious settlement.

Remember to:
- choose something from your own knowledge (e.g. recusants)
- stick to the dates in the question.

? Have I ***explained*** how the Act of Supremacy helped enforce the settlement?

? Have I provided a reason of my own to explain how the settlement was enforced?

? Have I ***supported*** my points with relevant evidence?

Review your skills

Check up

Review your response to the exam-style question on page 18. Tick ✓ the column below to show how well you think you have done each of the following.

	Had a go ✓	Nearly there ✓	Got it! ✓
carried out what the question asked	☐	☐	☐
made sure the information included was relevant	☐	☐	☐
covered everything in the question	☐	☐	☐

Note down three things you have learned that you will apply when using your own knowledge in answering history questions in future.

1. ....
2. ....
3. ....

Need more practice?

On separate paper, plan and write your response to the exam-style question below.

Exam-style question

Explain why the Elizabethan religious settlement made Elizabeth I more powerful.

You may include the following in your answer:

- the Act of Supremacy
- visitations.

You **must** also include information of your own. **(12 marks)**

How confident do you feel about each of these **skills**? Colour in the bars.

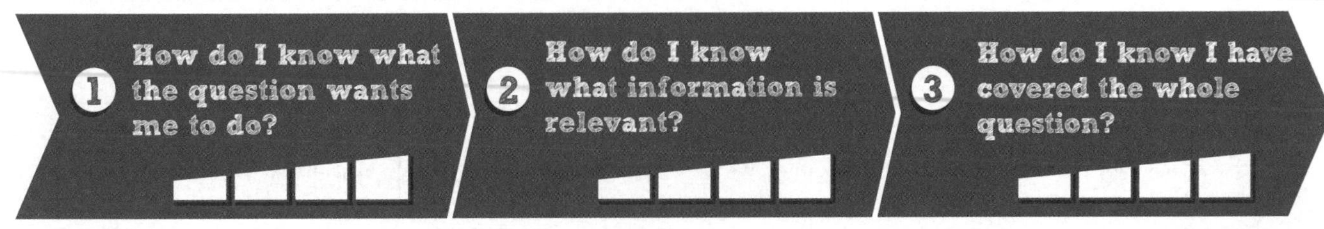

1 How do I know what the question wants me to do?
2 How do I know what information is relevant?
3 How do I know I have covered the whole question?

3 Making a judgement

Historians often argue about historical questions, such as was Elizabethan entertainment violent? This unit will help you to make your own, effective, informed judgements. Here 'informed' means showing an understanding of the facts. You will build the following skills:

- using historical evidence to make a judgement
- deciding what the 'right' judgement is
- how to deal with conflicting evidence.

Exam-style question

'Entertainment continued to be very violent during Elizabethan times.'
How far do you agree? Explain your answer.
You may use the following in you answer:

- cock-fighting
- theatres.

You **must** also include information of your own. **(16 marks)**

Generalisations do not make strong judgements because they ignore differences between people and places or changes over time. They assume everyone and everything is the same.

Sometimes generalisations are easy to spot because they use words like 'everyone' or 'no-one'; 'everywhere' or 'nowhere'; 'all', 'always' or 'never' – ***but sometimes they don't.***

We can't generalise about generalisations!

Here are some generalisations. Can you give reasons why they are not effective judgements?

- The weather is always colder in Scotland.
- Footballers are millionaires.
- Children are shorter than adults.
- The Elizabethan Religious Settlement was a success.

The three key questions in the **skills boosts** will help you to answer the following:

1 How do I make a judgement?

2 How do I know what the 'right' judgement is?

3 How do I deal with conflicting evidence?

Get started

Look at the exam-style question below, then at a student's plan of a possible answer.

Exam-style question

'Education made great progress in Elizabethan England.' How far do you agree? Explain your answer.

You may use the following in your answer:

- grammar schools
- universities.

You **must** also include information of your own. **(16 marks)**

	For	Against
Grammar schools	• *Lots of new grammar schools: 1560s = 42; 1570s = 30; every town in England had one by 1577* • *Some taught alternative curriculum for merchants and craftsmen*	• *Grammar schools were for boys only* • *Grammar schools had fees; families had to give up the income their sons might earn* • *Subjects focused a lot on Latin, Greek and learning by heart*
Lower classes	• *Petty schools* • *Dame schools* • *Apprenticeships – if you could afford them*	• *Taught basics only* • *Majority of children did not go to school at all, especially girls* • *Most children worked and learned how to do the family job or trade*
Girls' education	*Noble girls similar education to boys*	*Very limited – very few girls went to school* *Female literacy rates lower (10%) and didn't improve compared to male (rose from 20% to 30%)*
Conclusion		

1. How far does the evidence in the student plan agree with the statement in the exam-style question above that 'education made great progress in Elizabethan England'? Tick the phrase that best fits.

Agrees strongly	☐
Agrees more than disagrees	☐
Disagrees more than agrees	☐
Disagrees strongly?	☐

2. Write two sentences in the 'conclusion' row on the student's plan above to explain your choice.

Remember this?

Leisure and education in Elizabethan England

This unit uses the theme of leisure and education in Elizabethan England to build your skills in making a judgement. If you need to review your knowledge of this theme, work through these pages.

1. Tick which of these statements are true and which are false.

	true	false
a Only a small percentage of Elizabethan children went to school.		
b Literacy rates improved from 20% to 30% for all Elizabethans.		
c Protestants did not believe in education.		
d Girls from noble families went to school until they were 14 years old.		
e Girls went to Dame Schools.		
f Apprentices got paid very little.		

2. Complete this table to show who might go to which type of school and what they learned.

School	Who?	What did they learn?
No school		
Private tutors		
Dame schools		
Petty schools		
Grammar schools		
Apprenticeships		
University		

3 Tick who would take part in these Elizabethan leisure activities.

Activity	Upper class Female	Upper class Male	Working class Female	Working class Male
Hunting on horseback with hounds				
Real tennis				
Football				
Cock-fighting				
Theatre				
Listening to music at home				
Dancing				

4 Tick which of the following statements are true and which are false.

		true	false
a	Elizabeth I disliked cruel sports such as bear or bull baiting or cock-fighting.		
b	Most Elizabethans disapproved of gambling.		
c	Football was a violent, dangerous sport.		
d	Elizabethans disliked rude and vulgar humour.		
e	There was a great deal of new literature being published in Elizabethan England.		
f	Elizabethan England saw the first purpose-built theatres.		
g	Elizabeth I only approved of religious plays.		
h	A lot of new music was composed in Elizabethan England.		

5 Draw lines to match up the sentence beginnings to the sentence ends.

Beginnings	Ends
A Elizabeth I being Protestant led to lots of new plays being written …	a … because the audience didn't know their endings.
B New plays were not about Bible stories and were extremely popular …	b … because it was the first purpose-built theatre.
C The Red Lion, built in Whitechapel in 1567, was famous …	c … because sometimes 2,000 people queued to see a performance.
D Going to the theatre was clearly a very popular pastime in Elizabethan England …	d … because traditional 'mystery plays' were banned for being too Catholic.

6 Write a sentence to explain why the increase in new plays led to an increase in new music in Elizabethan England.

How do I make a judgement?

You will often be asked how far you agree with something, or how far something is true. To make your judgement, you must look at evidence both for and against before you make up your mind.

A ? Education made great progress in Elizabethan England.

B ? But grammar schools were not available to most children.

C ? Literacy rates improved but not much.

D ? University education was extremely limited.

1. Speeches B, C and D are challenging A's point of view that education made great progress in Elizabethan England. Note down a piece of evidence to support each of B, C and D.

B ....

C ....

D ....

2. The table below lists evidence to support the point of view of speech A. How strong is the evidence? Tick the box you agree with.

Evidence	Very strong	Quite strong	Slightly strong
Literacy rates for males increased from 20% to 30%, although they remained at 10% for females.			
Lots of grammar schools were founded: 72 in the 1560s and 1570s.			
New colleges were founded at both universities. For example Elizabeth I founded Jesus College at Oxford University.			

3. Overall, which do you find more convincing: the evidence for or against the point of view that education made strong progress in Elizabethan England? Give reasons below.

....

....

....

....

....

....

2 How do I know what the 'right' judgement is?

Before you make a judgement about something, you will need to look at evidence for and against it. This will help to make your judgement effective and informed.

1. Read the student's notes below then tick ✓ the column in the table that you think matches these notes best.

Bear baiting – bears tied to poles while dogs attacked them; many dogs killed; very popular – Elizabeth I liked it; special arenas built

Theatre – Elizabethans loved plays, new theatres built, e.g. Red Lion, Whitechapel; thousands would queue for a performance; comedies popular – rude humour

Football – no rules, dangerous games; sometimes players were killed; pitches in streets and countryside

What?	Very violent	Quite violent	Not violent	It depends
Bear baiting				
Theatre				
Football				

2. Now you have completed task 1 what judgement can you make about this statement: 'Entertainment continued to be very violent during Elizabethan times.' Use the value continuum below to mark on ↑ what you think.

Disagree 100%	Disagree strongly	Disagree more than agree	Agree more than disagree	Agree strongly	Agree 100%

You can use these words and phrases when making a judgement on how far you agree with something. Remember to avoid generalisations.
to some extent …
to a large extent …
to a small extent …
very / not very / quite / some / strongly / overwhelmingly / largely / hardly

3. Rewrite ✎ this generalisation to make an effective judgement.

'Elizabethan entertainment needed to be violent to be popular.'

3 How do I deal with conflicting evidence?

Writing about how far you agree with something when there is conflicting evidence – evidence for and against – can be tricky. You need to deal with both sides to answer the question properly.

Exam-style question

'The growth of theatre was the biggest change to Elizabethan leisure.' How far do you agree?

Look at the following research notes written by a student:

Plays: lots of new plays written, huge demand – new theatre companies formed; first purpose-built theatre built (Red Lion, Whitechapel 1567); theatre = cheap as 1d; sometimes 2,000 people queued so theatre growing greatly; new theatre companies (e.g. The Queen's Men 1583)

Music: new music – being composed to go with new, non-religious plays at theatre

Books: lots of new literature, plus translations of Latin and Greek classics; male literacy up by half

1. Does the evidence show the growth of theatre to be the biggest change to Elizabethan leisure? Tick either the 'Yes' or 'No' column. If 'Sometimes. It depended on …' then explain why.

	Yes?	No?	Sometimes. It depended on …
Plays			
Music			
Books			

The evidence is conflicting. It shows that not only theatre grew a lot.

2. Look at the words and phrases in the text box then write where they should be used in the student answer below:

……………………… *Elizabethan England saw the first purpose-built theatres, but* ……………………… *there was also a great deal of new literature written, so this changed leisure too.*

Conflicting evidence

Useful words and phrases:

On the one hand … but on the other …

It is true that … it is also true …

… although … … however …

3. Look at the notes above about music. Use some of the words and phrases above to help you show how there was a lot of new music composed in Elizabethan England – but much of it was also due to the growth of theatre.

………………………………………………………………………………………………

………………………………………………………………………………………………

………………………………………………………………………………………………

………………………………………………………………………………………………

Sample response

Exam-style question

'Entertainment continued to be very violent during Elizabethan times.'
How far do you agree? Explain your answer.

You may use the following in your answer:

- baiting
- literature.

You **must** also use information of your own. **(16 marks)**

Below is part of a student's answer to the exam-style question.

1. Highlight in different colours the evidence for and against the statement in the question.
2. Circle and annotate the words and phrases that the student is using to deal with conflicting evidence – where there is evidence both for and against the statement.

Much Elizabethan entertainment was violent. Baiting, for example, was very popular and most towns had a bull ring where dogs were set upon a chained bull. Cock-fighting was also enjoyed by Elizabethans, even Queen Elizabeth, as was bear baiting. When football was played there were no rules and players could even be killed. On the other hand, real tennis became popular too, although only rich men would play. Other popular sports included hunting and wrestling, which could both be said to be violent.

It is also true, however, that literature became increasingly popular in Elizabethan England so not all entertainment was violent. Accounts of voyages of discovery were in demand and most well-educated people wrote poetry. These things were only possible for the wealthy. Theatre, on the other hand, was available to everyone as even poor people could pay 1d to stand and watch a play. Sometimes there were queues of 2,000 people. As there were so many new plays written, and new music composed to go with them, it cannot be true to say that entertainment continued to be very violent as some changes show less violent pastimes were becoming more popular.

Your turn!

Look at the following exam-style question and the student plan.

Exam-style question

'The most important change in leisure activities during the Elizabethan period was the growth of theatre.'

How far do you agree? Explain your answer.

Elizabethan theatre

For

- *Popular with all classes – sometimes queues of 2,000 people*
- *Plays = for all classes too, & comedies very popular – rude humour*
- *Only cost 1 penny to stand in front of stage so poor could afford to go*

Against

- *To be actor, needed to be a man and be able to read, and lots of people illiterate*

1 Write a paragraph about the importance of the growth of the theatre using the student plan to help you. Then add a judgement explaining how important you think it was.

Review your skills

Check up

Review your response to the exam-style question on page 29. Tick the column to show how well you think you have done each of the following.

	Had a go	Nearly there	Got it!
used evidence to make a judgement			
decided on my judgement			
dealt with conflicting evidence			
avoided generalisations			

Look over all of your work in this unit. Note down three things you have learned that you will do when you have to answer a question that asks you how far you agree with something.

1 ....

2 ....

3 ....

Need more practice?

On separate paper, plan and write your response to the exam-style question below.

Exam-style question

'Education continued to only be available to very few in Elizabethan England.'

How far do you agree? Explain your answer.

You may use the following in your answer:

- apprenticeships
- girls' education.

You **must** also use information of your own. **(16 marks)**

How confident do you feel about each of these **skills**? Colour in the bars below.

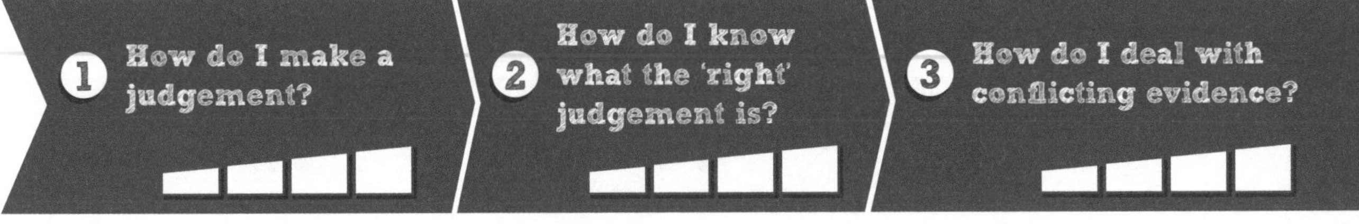

1 How do I make a judgement?
2 How do I know what the 'right' judgement is?
3 How do I deal with conflicting evidence?

Paragraphing and structure

Getting your ideas and knowledge across effectively is important. Longer answers need to be written in a logical order and clearly linked to the question. The skills you will build in this unit are to:

- organise your ideas into an effective order
- build strong paragraphs
- stay focused on the question.

In the exam, you will be asked to tackle questions like the one below. This unit will prepare you to write your own response to this type of question.

Exam-style question

Explain why Mary, Queen of Scots was executed in 1587.

You may use the following in your answer:

- the papal bull of excommunication (1570)
- the Babington plot (1586).

You **must** also include information of your own. **(12 marks)**

A useful way of organising your answer is to PEEL your paragraphs. This stands for:

Point	What is the paragraph about? What point will it make?
Explain	Develop the explanation in more detail.
Evidence	What historical examples and facts can you use to back up your point?
Link	Link back to the question to reinforce your point.

This approach will help you stay focused on the question by **linking your point** back to the question at the end of each paragraph.

Tips for linking back

1. Use the wording in the question to make sure you keep focused.
2. When you link back, you can also add some analysis, saying what this link might mean. Here is a suggestion: How important is the point you have made in explaining the question focus?

The three key questions in the skills boosts will help you learn to organise your ideas and produce a strong, focused essay.

 How do I organise my ideas into an effective order?

 How do I build strong paragraphs?

 How do I stay focused on the question?

Look at this exam-style question and the student's plan for what to include in an answer.

Exam-style question

Explain why Mary, Queen of Scots was a danger to Elizabeth I in the years 1568–1587.

You may use the following in your answer:

- the Duke of Norfolk
- the Babington plot.

You **must** also use information of your own. **(12 marks)**

1 *Mary, Queen of Scots → England 1568*
2 *Northern Rebellion – Duke of Norfolk to marry Mary, Queen of Scots 1569*
Mary, Queen of Scots = Catholic + claim to throne is strong
3 *Papal excommunication → Catholics a threat*
Mary, Queen of Scots = Catholic rival, strong claim to throne 1570
4 *Ridolfi plot – Duke of Norfolk to depose Elizabeth I, marry Mary, Queen of Scots so Catholic queen 1571*
5 *Catholic priests start arriving in England 1574 – Mary, Queen of Scots greater threat?*
6 *Throckmorton plot – put Mary, Queen of Scots on throne; French and Spanish backing 1583*
7 *1585 threat to Elizabeth I worse – Elizabeth supported Dutch against Spain; France + Spain = allies*
8 *Babington plot 1586 wanted to put Mary, Queen of Scots on throne again; Mary, Queen of Scots is in on the plot!*
9 *1587 Mary, Queen of Scots executed after rumours of Spanish landing in Wales*

1 Using the student notes above:

a highlight any mentions of Mary, Queen of Scots

b highlight in another colour where there is any mention of the bullet point prompts given in the question

c circle any information of the student's own

d underline anything that is repeated.

2 This student has decided to answer the question chronologically. Time is limited in an exam. Suggest one way in which planning to answer a question chronologically may lead to problems.

....

....

....

It is important to plan your answer well. A good structure to your plan can help you write a better answer.

Remember this?

Plots and rebellions

This unit uses the theme of plots and rebellions to build your skills in paragraphing and structuring your answers. If you need to review your knowledge of this theme, work through these pages.

1. Here are some events that took place in Elizabeth I's reign. Starting with the earliest one, number each event in chronological order. Write the date alongside each event.

Babington plot Date: .... ☐	Ridolfi plot Date: .... ☐	The Spanish Armada Date: .... ☐
Papal bull of excommunication Date: .... ☐	Mary, Queen of Scots came to England Date: .... ☐	Catholic priests began arriving in England Date: .... ☐
Northern Rebellion Date: .... ☐	Execution of Mary, Queen of Scots Date: .... ☐	Throckmorton plot Date: .... ☐

2. Tick whether you think the following statements are true or false.

	true	false
a Elizabeth I and Mary, Queen of Scots were both granddaughters of Henry VII.	☐	☐
b Elizabeth I was determined to execute Mary, Queen of Scots after the Babington plot.	☐	☐
c Mary, Queen of Scots was half French.	☐	☐
d Mary, Queen of Scots fled to England from Scotland in 1568.	☐	☐

3. Draw a line linking each answer to the right question.

A Sheltering Catholic priests was made punishable by death	a What happened as a result of the Babington plot?
B Over 11,000 Catholics were imprisoned or put under surveillance	b What happened as a result of the Throckmorton plot?
C Mary, Queen of Scots was executed	c Who ran a large spy network for Elizabeth I's government?
D Priest holes	d How did wealthy Catholics protect Catholic priests?
E Sir Francis Walsingham	e What law was introduced in 1585?

4 Give two reasons why Mary, Queen of Scots was a threat to Elizabeth I.

1 ....

2 ....

5 Look at the statements **A–G**. Sort the statements under the correct plot in the table. One has been done for you already. Some of the statements might belong to more than one plot.

A Philip II would supply 10,000 soldiers from the Netherlands.

B Letters about the plot written in code were sent to Mary, Queen of Scots.

C Norfolk was involved in the plot.

D Six Catholics were prepared to assassinate Elizabeth I.

E The French Duke of Guise would invade and free his cousin, Mary, Queen of Scots.

F The Duke of Guise would supply 60,000 men.

G Spain, France and the pope supported this plot.

Ridolfi plot 1571	Throckmorton plot 1583	Babington plot 1586
A		

6 Briefly explain how the Act for the Preservation of the Queen's Safety (1585) helped lead to the execution of Mary, Queen of Scots.

....

....

....

....

7 Complete the paragraph below by writing in the words from the word box in the correct places.

John Hart	pardon	torture	special prison	over 30 towns
neighbours	ciphers	130 priests	nobility	every county

Walsingham had spies in .... in England and .... abroad. He also paid ordinary people for information so many spied on their .... Other methods he used included .... and .... Even the .... were under suspicion.

Not all Catholic priests were executed and a .... was built to keep them in. .... was a Catholic priest who spied for Walsingham in return for a .... However, ... and 60 of their supporters were executed.

How do I organise my ideas into an effective order?

The best way to write a strong history essay is to be clear about what you think the answer is before you begin writing the essay. This skills boost will help you to organise your ideas into the best order.

Look at this student's planning notes for the exam-style question on page 31. The points have been numbered as the student thought of them.

Mary, Queen of Scots executed 1587: Explain!

1 *Papal bull: Catholics not to obey Elizabeth I*
To overthrow Elizabeth I = good deed

2 *1587: Mary, Queen of Scots executed*
Elizabeth I reluctant to execute but rumours Spanish troops had landed January 1587

3 *Babington 1586 aim = Mary, Queen of Scots → throne*
Mary, Queen of Scots involved – letters evidence
Timing: Spain threatening England

4 *Other plots: Mary, Queen of Scots → Throckmorton 1583*

5 *Spain threatened England*
1587 – relations bad, worse 1585;
Armada planned, aim = overthrow Elizabeth I; if Mary, Queen of Scots alive she → queen

This student has decided to plan their answer around two themes: Spanish threats and plots.

1. Add the information from the notes above into the table below using the themes provided to help.

Spanish threats	Plots

By organising information into themes it gives an overall structure to your response and helps place details into an effective order.

2. Add the following events to the themes in the table above.
   - **a** The Treaty of Joinville
   - **b** Catholic priests arriving in England

3. Circle the theme you think is the most important reason for the execution of Mary, Queen of Scots in 1587.

How do I build strong paragraphs?

Once your ideas are written down and you have decided what the theme of each paragraph is, you need to make sure that your paragraphs are organised too. This skills boost will help you do this.

Read the exam-style question again.

Exam-style question

Explain why Mary, Queen of Scots was a danger to Elizabeth I in the years 1568–1587.

You may use the following in your answer:

- the Duke of Norfolk
- the Babington plot.

You **must** also use information of your own. **(12 marks)**

① The PEEL method of organising a paragraph has been done for the papal bull of 1570. Do the same for the Babington plot by filling in the end column of the table.

PEEL	Papal bull (1570)	Babington plot (1586)
Point: gives a clear reason	The papal bull of 1570 made Mary, Queen of Scots more of a danger to Elizabeth, as it encouraged Catholics to plot against her.	
Explanation: shows how reason answers question	Catholics' loyalty to Elizabeth I no longer certain. Mary, Queen of Scots prisoner in England since 1568. Catholic rival to Elizabeth I, she has a strong claim to throne so is a great threat.	
Evidence: supports and strengthens explanation	Ridolfi plot came soon after it in 1571. Catholic priests began arriving in England from 1574 to encourage Catholics to obey the pope. Other plots too.	
Link back: reinforces the point and keeps answer focused on question	Therefore papal bull made Catholics' loyalty uncertain and encouraged plots supporting Mary, Queen of Scots. By 1587 there had been several attempts to replace Elizabeth with Mary.	

3 How do I stay focused on the question?

This skills booster will help you to stay focused on the question and avoid wandering off the point.

Keep referring back to the question focus in your answer. One way to do this is, at the end of each paragraph, write a sentence linking it back to the question. If you can't, you have probably wandered off the point.

Below is a student's paragraph from an answer to the following exam-style question.

Exam-style question

Explain why Mary, Queen of Scots was a danger to Elizabeth I between 1568–1587.

Another reason why Mary, Queen of Scots was a danger to Elizabeth I was the threat from Spain. It was very serious by 1584 when the Treaty of Joinville was signed, uniting France and Spain against Protestantism. By 1586, when the Babington plot to put Mary on the throne with Spanish and French support was uncovered, England was fighting Spain in the Netherlands and Drake was attacking Spanish colonies in the New World. This led Philip to decide to invade England. Although Mary was dead by the time of the Armada, her execution gave Spain another excuse to attack. So Spain made Mary, Queen of Scots a threat to Elizabeth I because ...

1 a Highlight mentions of the question focus: Mary, Queen of Scots.

b Circle the question wording that is referred to.

c Which of the following statements would be the best to complete the paragraph, linking it back to the question? Tick the relevant box.

i Mary, Queen of Scots had a claim to the English throne. ☐

ii Mary, Queen of Scots was supported by the Spanish in plots to overthrow Elizabeth I. ☐

iii Spain was much stronger than England. ☐

Here is another exam-style question and a paragraph from a student answer.

Exam-style question

'Mary, Queen of Scots was the greatest danger facing Elizabeth I.' How far do you agree?

Although Mary, Queen of Scots was a great danger to Elizabeth I, Spain could be said to be more important. It supported Mary, Queen of Scots in numerous plots, which made them more serious because Spain was very wealthy and, from 1584, allied with France against Protestantism. The greatest threat faced by Elizabeth I, the Armada, was launched by Spain. ...

2 a Highlight mentions of the focus of the question (Mary) and the focus of the paragraph (Spain).

b Finish the last sentence of the student's paragraph to give a judgement saying how important Spain was as a danger compared with Mary, Queen of Scots and why.

So, Spain was .... threat to Elizabeth I than

Mary, Queen of Scots because ....

....

Sample response

Here is an extract from an essay by a student who rushed straight into answering the question below. You will have to decide what skills they have shown and give some advice.

Exam-style question

Explain why Mary, Queen of Scots was executed in 1587.

You may use the following in your answer:

- the papal bull of excommunication (1570)
- the Babington plot (1586).

You **must** also include information of your own. **(12 marks)**

Mary, Queen of Scots was executed in 1587 because of the Babington plot to put her on the throne instead of Elizabeth I. Mary, Queen of Scots had been in England since 1568 and had a strong claim to the English throne, which is a political reason she was dangerous. And the 1570 papal bull of excommunication said that Catholics ought to depose Elizabeth I, which shows religious reasons were important too. There were other plots like Ridolfi and Throckmorton too. Babington was serious because the Duke of Guise planned to invade England with 60,000 troops. Six Catholics were prepared to kill Elizabeth. When the Babington plot was made, England was under threat from Spain. The Ridolfi plot had come soon after the papal bull and was to make Mary queen of England. Philip II supported this plot. After Babington and before Mary was executed there were rumours that Spanish troops had landed in Wales. Mary was dangerous because she could take Elizabeth I's throne and she had support from Catholics at home and abroad.

Francis Walsingham was an important reason why Mary was executed. He intercepted letters between Babington and Mary, Queen of Scots, and the Privy Council tried and convicted her of planning to assassinate Elizabeth I. Walsingham also uncovered the Throckmorton plot.

1. Read through this answer and highlight anything that is about, or could be linked to, the papal bull of excommunication in one colour. Then, in another colour, do the same for the Babington plot.

2. Complete this table by ticking to show what skills the student has used.

Skill	Paragraph 1	Paragraph 2
Made a clear point at the start of the paragraph.		
Clearly explained how the reason given answers the question.		
Provided supporting evidence.		
Organised the information in the paragraphs into a logical order.		
Linked back to the question at the end of the paragraph.		

3. What tips would you give the student to help them improve their answer? Try to write three tips.

Your turn!

You are going to write two paragraphs as part of your own answer to the exam-style question on page 38. One paragraph will be on one of the prompts (the papal bull or the Babington plot). The other paragraph will be on another reason for Mary, Queen of Scots' execution such as: England's relations with Spain in the run-up to her execution, or the Guise family.

?
Have I remembered to organise my material into paragraphs?

?
Have I remembered to PEEL my paragraphs?

?
Have I answered the question?

Get back on track

Review your skills

Check up

Review your response to the exam-style question on page 38. Tick ✓ the column to show how well you think you have done each of the following.

	Had a go ✓	Nearly there ✓	Got it! ✓
Organised my ideas into an effective order	☐	☐	☐
Built strong paragraphs	☐	☐	☐
Linked back to the question	☐	☐	☐

Look over all of your work in this unit. Note down three things you have learned to do to structure your answer.

1. ....
2. ....
3. ....

Need more practice?

On a separate piece of paper, plan and write your response to the exam-style question below.

Exam-style question

Explain why Elizabeth I was under threat from her Catholic subjects, 1569–1587.

You may use the following in your answer:

- the papal bull of excommunication
- Mary, Queen of Scots.

You **must** also use information of your own. **(12 marks)**

How confident do you feel about each of these **skills**? Colour in the bars.

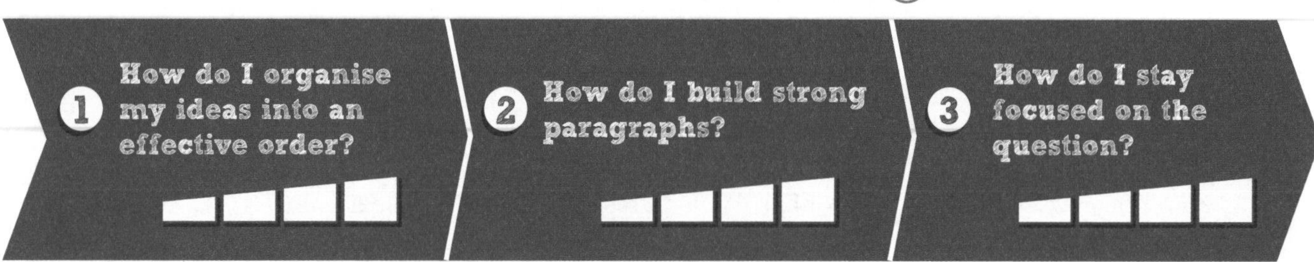

1 How do I organise my ideas into an effective order?
2 How do I build strong paragraphs?
3 How do I stay focused on the question?

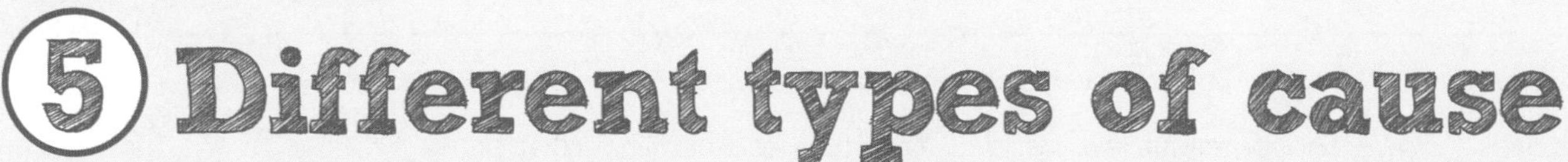

5 Different types of cause

Historians gather a lot of evidence. They need to understand what this evidence reveals about why something happened or about its impact. They organise the evidence, examine it carefully, then draw conclusions from it. This is analysis. This unit will help you develop your analytical skills by:

- making sense of historical causes through analysis
- identifying different types of cause
- dealing with causes that fit into more than one category.

In the exam, you will be asked to tackle questions like the one below. This unit will prepare you to write your own response to this type of question.

Exam-style question

'Religion caused the decline in Anglo–Spanish relations 1567–1580.' How far do you agree? Explain your answer.

You may use the following in your answer:

- Francis Drake
- The Netherlands

You **must** also use information of your own. **(16 marks)**

The shapes to the right could be organised in various ways, such as according to colour or shape. You could rearrange them to make it easier to answer questions like:

- How many shapes are blue?
- How many shapes are quadrangles?
- How many shapes have five points?

Imagine that every shape is a piece of historical evidence (fact, event, etc.). Organising the evidence (chronologically or by theme) helps us to draw conclusions about, or analyse, important questions such as why Anglo–Spanish relations declined.

The three key questions in the **skills boosts** will help you analyse causes to produce strong exam answers.

1. How do I make sense of lots of different causes?
2. How do I decide what type of cause something is?
3. How do I deal with different types of causes?

Get started

Evidence can be organised chronologically or by theme. Useful themes include the following:

Political: power, government, law, policies, treaties, international relations

Religious: religious beliefs, different religions such as Catholic or Protestant

Economic: money, wealth, making money, employment, taxation, trade, prices

Social: how society is organised, family, housing, education, leisure, health

Now look at the exam-style question from page 41. Here are a student's first thoughts on what to include in the answer to this question.

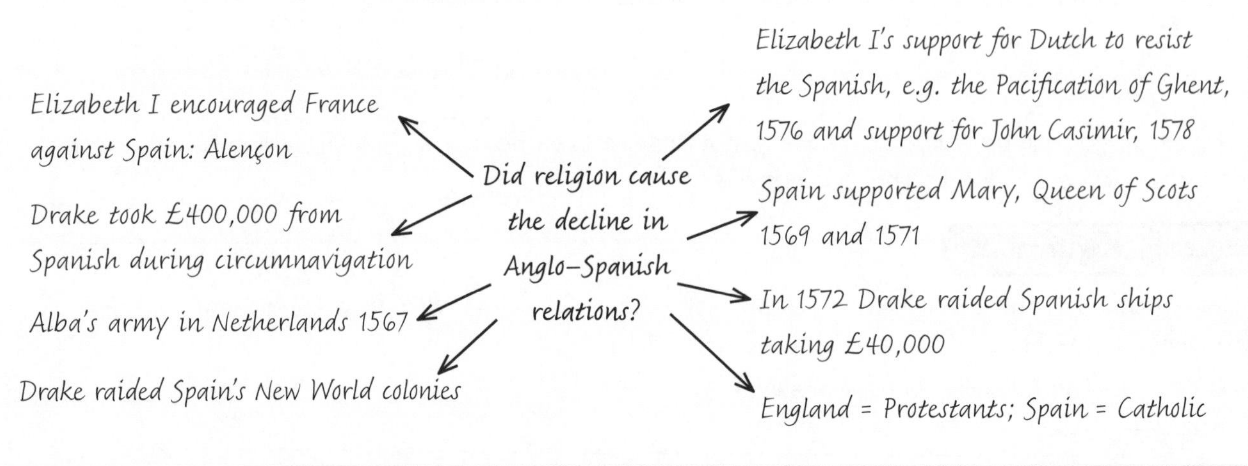

Did religion cause the decline in Anglo–Spanish relations?
Elizabeth I encouraged France against Spain: Alençon
Drake took £400,000 from Spanish during circumnavigation
Alba's army in Netherlands 1567
Drake raided Spain's New World colonies
Elizabeth I's support for Dutch to resist the Spanish, e.g. the Pacification of Ghent, 1576 and support for John Casimir, 1578
Spain supported Mary, Queen of Scots 1569 and 1571
In 1572 Drake raided Spanish ships taking £40,000
England = Protestants; Spain = Catholic

The essay began with the top left point ('Elizabeth I encouraged France ...') and then worked its way around each in a clockwise direction.

1. Suggest reasons why this approach would not be a good one.

2. Using three different coloured highlighters, highlight the student's ideas about:
   a. the New World problem
   b. the Netherlands
   c. Spain's support for Mary, Queen of Scots.

3. Decide which points you think are most important and reorganise the plan for the student in the space below.

Elizabeth's foreign policy

This unit uses the theme of Elizabeth's foreign policy to develop your analytical skills. If you need to review your knowledge of this theme, work through these pages.

1. Look at this table. Draw a line to match the beginnings of each sentence with its correct ending.

A The New World made Spain very wealthy …	a … armed ships that captured other ships and cargoes.
B Privateers were merchants with …	b … huge quantities of silver.
C Spain's American colonies supplied it with …	c … Elizabeth I knighted him on the deck of the *Golden Hind*.
D When Drake returned from circumnavigating the globe …	d … because she wanted to improve relations with Spain.
E Elizabeth I did not publicly welcome Drake home in 1572 …	e … because of all the silver, tobacco, sugar and spices there were.

2. Complete the statements by ticking the correct ending. There might be more than one solution.

a Drake's circumnavigation …
- i … improved relations with Spain. ☐
- ii … boosted Elizabeth I's finances. ☐
- iii … was welcomed by Philip II of Spain. ☐
- iv … defied Spain's claim to own the New World. ☐

b In 1566 the Netherlands …
- i … belonged to Spain. ☐
- ii … rebelled against Spanish rule. ☐
- iii … was an independent country. ☐
- iv … was made up of both Catholic and Protestant provinces. ☐

3. Read the following statements and tick which are true, and which are false.

	true	false
a Relations between France and England worsened in the 1570s.	☐	☐
b Elizabeth I gave Drake secret orders to attack Spanish colonies in the New World in 1577.	☐	☐
c The Netherlands rebellion in 1566 was about Spain forcing it to be Catholic.	☐	☐
d Philip II persecuted Protestants in the Netherlands.	☐	☐
e Elizabeth I offered the promise of marriage to the Duke of Alençon.	☐	☐

4. Explain what caused the Spanish Fury in 1576.

....

....

....

5 Explain the effect the sack of Antwerp had in November 1576.

....

....

....

6 Tick which of the following were **not** called for in the Pacification of Ghent in 1576.

a Religious persecution in the Netherlands was to stop. ☐

b The Netherlands were to be completely independent from Spain. ☐

c All Spanish troops were to leave the Netherlands. ☐

d The Netherlands were to be allowed to run their own affairs but still belonged to Spain. ☐

7 This table lists some events that took place in the Netherlands in 1578 and 1579. For each event tick the box showing which year it happened.

Event	1578	1579
a The Duke of Alençon led an army into the Netherlands		
b Spain's armies began making progress in the Netherlands		
c The Dutch provinces were united against the Spanish		
d The Duke of Alençon withdrew from the Netherlands		
e The Catholic provinces of the Netherlands made peace with Spain		

8 Explain what the Privy Council wanted Elizabeth I to do in 1578.

....

9 Here are some events that all happened between 1570 and 1580. Add a date to each event then number them in the correct order.

The Pacification of Ghent
Date: ....
Event order: ....

Elizabeth I sent mercenaries to the Netherlands
Date: ....
Event order: ....

Alençon withdrew from the Netherlands
Date: ....
Event order: ....

The Spanish Fury
Date: ....
Event order: ....

The Dutch Protestants asked Alençon for help
Date: ....
Event order: ....

The Duke of Parma began making strong progress in the Netherlands
Date: ....
Event order: ....

Catholic provinces made peace with Spain
Date: ....
Event order: ....

How do I make sense of lots of different causes?

Analysing why a historical event happened means:

- **Step 1** Gathering evidence
- **Step 2** Organising the evidence
- **Step 3** Drawing conclusions from the evidence as to what caused it.

This skills builder will help you to practise this.

1. **Step 1: Gathering evidence**

Read the student's notes listing reasons why the Spanish Armada failed to invade England in 1588. Cross out (~~cat~~) the information that is not relevant as a reason.

A The English conserved cannonballs for the decisive battle	B Elizabeth I let her commanders make naval decisions	C English galleons were faster and more mobile
D Poor communication between Sidonia's and Parma's fleets	E It took Parma 48 hours to prepare his ships	F The English stopped Medina Sidonia anchoring off the Isle of Wight
G English cannon and gun decks were better designed	H Spanish ships had poor quality cannonballs and supplies	I English ships could fire six times more cannonballs than Spanish
J English fireships created havoc	K Parma had lots of small ships	L Storms scattered the Armada
M Philip II had received support from the Pope	N There were delays of 10 weeks before the Spanish ships set sail	O Two Spanish ships were captured off Plymouth

2. **Step 2: Organising the evidence**

   a. Highlight in one colour the student's evidence showing Spain's mistakes.

   b. Highlight in another colour the evidence showing the English had better tactics.

3. **Step 3: Drawing conclusions**

   a. How true is it that the Armada failed because of Spain's mistakes rather than England's tactics? Using the evidence above, show your decision on the value line below using an arrow (↑).

100% England	Mainly England	England more than Spain	Spain more than England	Mainly Spain	100% Spain

   b. Explain your decision.

....

....

....

....

....

2 How do I decide what type of cause something is?

Historians often describe causes as political, religious, economic or social. This can be a very helpful way of analysing historical events. This skills builder will help you to do this.

Look at the exam-style question on page 41. It suggests that religion was to blame for the decline in relations between England and Spain 1567–1580.

1. Read the two key facts about the declining relations between England and Spain below. Are these reasons: political (P), religious (R), economic (E) or social (S)? Write P, R, E or S, according to which you think **best** fits.

a **Netherlands 1567–1580**

England gave support to Dutch rebels. Many were Protestant. Philip II wanted to stamp out Protestantism and the rebellion. Elizabeth I was concerned at having a large Catholic army nearby. Philip II was prepared to use it in the Ridolfi plot.

b **Francis Drake 1567–1580**

Drake traded illegally with Spain's New World colonies and raided Spanish ships and settlements. Elizabeth I backed him. Drake made them both a lot of money. He sailed around the globe and claimed a region of North America for England.

2. Sort this student's notes on the exam-style question on page 41 into political, religious or economic causes. Write the letter of the cause in the appropriate box below. Letters can be put in more than one box. One has been done for you.

<u>*Netherlands*</u>

A *1567: Spain sent large army under Alba to stamp out rebellion and heresy (Protestantism) – Elizabeth I facing Catholic threat; plots in 1569, 1571 – Alba's army included in plans*

B *1576: Pacification of Ghent treaty – Elizabeth I supported Dutch against Spain and agreed to send armed forces later*

C *1578: Spain went back on treaty. Elizabeth I sent John Casimir and mercenaries; they attacked Dutch Catholic churches; Catholics made peace with Spain, Protestants fought on*

<u>*Drake*</u>

D *1570–1571 Drake captured lots of Spanish ships and cargo; in 1572 he captured £40,000 of silver in Panama*

E *1577–1580 Drake circumnavigated the globe – plundered Spanish ports and ships along coast of Chile, Peru – captured £400,000 of Spanish treasure*

F *1580 Elizabeth I knighted Drake on board Golden Hind, angering Philip II who considered Drake a pirate*

Political

A

Religious

Economic

3 How do I deal with different types of causes?

In skills boost (2) you might have found it difficult to decide if something was religious or political, for example. This skills booster will show you how to deal with this problem.

Read the following extracts from student answers analysing the decline in Anglo–Spanish relations.

Extract A

In 1567 Anglo–Spanish relations declined because Spain sent Alba to the Netherlands with a large army to stamp out heresy (Protestantism), which also threatened England's security. This is religious and political. Soon after, in 1569 and 1571, Catholic plots against Elizabeth I were developed that included Alba's army in their plans to support England's Catholics. This means it was religious. However, it was also political.

Extract B

Politics and religion often combined to cause a decline in Anglo–Spanish relations. In 1567, Spain sent Alba's army to the Netherlands to stamp out heresy (Protestantism), which threatened England's security. The threat grew in 1569 and 1571 when there were Catholic plots to overthrow Elizabeth I involving Alba's army. These events in the decline in Anglo–Spanish relations were both political and religious because they involved the overthrow of Elizabeth I to replace her with a Catholic monarch.

(1) a Highlight the words and phrases in Extracts A and B that identify the role played by religion and politics in the decline of Anglo–Spanish relations. Use one colour highlight for religion and another for politics.

b How are these extracts different? Which is more effective – A or B? Write your thoughts.

Which answer reads like a list?

....

....

....

1570–1571 Drake captured lots of Spanish ships and cargo; in 1572 he captured £40,000 of silver in Panama

(2) The student has decided that Point D from the plan on page 46 is both a political and economic reason for a decline in Anglo–Spanish relations. Write an explanation of why this might be the case. Use Extract B above as guidance.

....

....

....

....

....

Sample response

Look again at the exam-style question on page 41, then read the extract from the student's full answer below. Here the student identifies different causes for the decline. But how strong an answer is it?

Francis Drake attacked Spanish shipping and colonies. In 1572, for example, he returned from Panama with £40,000 of Spanish silver, angering Philip II. This is an economic reason for worsening Anglo–Spanish relations. Drake's actions also defied Spain's power in America. This is political. Later, Drake became a national hero for circumnavigating the globe. He was only the second person in history to do this.

In 1577 Drake set out with orders from Elizabeth I to attack Spanish colonies to send a message that England would not be dominated by Spain. There were also fears of a Spanish invasion. This is political. He plundered the coastlines of Chile and Peru before returning with £400,000 of Spanish treasure. This is economic. It is also political because it is defying Spain's power in America. Drake circumnavigated the globe and was knighted by Elizabeth I. This was a message of defiance to Spain too and political.

1 Decide which descriptions below best fit the extract. Think about the following questions and then tick ✓ the appropriate box in the table below.

? Is there an explanation?

? Is there analysis?

? Is the answer well organised throughout?

Skill	Weak	✓	Strong	✓
Explanation	Narrative with some examples		Explains reasons for decline	
Evidence	Vague, imprecise, not very accurate		Accurate, specific and precise	
Organisation	None: hard to follow		Yes: chronological or by theme	
Analysis	A list of reasons with 'economic' or 'political' added on		Organised according to political and economic causes	

2 Give ✎ the student feedback on how to improve the answer. You can bullet point your comments.

Your turn!

You are going to write the next section of the answer to the exam-style question on page 41 to explain the decline in Anglo-Spanish relations in the years 1567–1580. You can use some of the suggestions below to help you.

A Elizabeth I helped Protestant rebels in Scotland and France in 1560–1561 and 1562–1564. Then Spain imposed a trade embargo and so did England.

B Elizabeth I helped the Dutch rebels in the Netherlands with money and mercenaries, e.g. £100,000 in 1576 and John Casimir in 1578.

C Philip II wanted to stamp out heresy (Protestantism) in the Netherlands. He also supported the Northern Rebellion and the Ridolfi plot.

D England encouraged France in the Netherlands, e.g. supporting Alençon's army.

E Elizabeth I allowed Dutch rebels (Sea Beggars) to attack Spanish shipping in the Channel

F Philip II sent a huge army to the Netherlands in 1567, just across the Channel from England.

1. Before you start writing, use this table to help you think about the different types of causes shown in the evidence. Tick which type of cause you think each of suggestions A–F relate to.

	A	B	C	D	E	F
Political						
Economic						
Religious						

2. Re-read Extract B from page 47 before you begin to write your next section of the answer below.

Get back on track

Review your skills

Check up

Review your response to the exam-style question on page 41. Tick the column to show how well you think you have done each of the following:

	Had a go	Nearly there	Got it!
made sense of different causes			
decided what type of cause something is			
dealt with different types of causes			
supported the points with evidence			

Look over all of your work in this unit. Note down three things you have learned that you will do when you have to answer a question that asks you to analyse an event or period by considering its causes.

1. ....
2. ....
3. ....

Need more practice?

On a separate piece of paper, plan and write your response to the exam-style question below.

Exam-style question

'Politics was the most important cause for the decline in Anglo–Spanish relations 1570–1580.' How far do you agree? Explain your answer.

You may use the following in your answer:

- privateers
- the Netherlands.

You **must** also use information of your own. (16 marks)

How confident do you feel about each of these **skills**? Colour in the bars.

1. How do I make sense of lots of different causes?
2. How do I decide what type of cause something is?
3. How do I deal with different types of causes?

Get started

6 Analysis by time frame

This unit will help you develop the skills to use a time frame effectively. You will be able to:

- identify long-term, short-term and trigger causes
- use chronology to help analyse how causes built up to an event
- use long-term and short-term causes effectively to plan an answer.

Here is an example of an exam-style question that asks you to look at causation:

Exam-style question

Explain why Philip II had decided, by the end of 1585, to prepare an Armada to invade England.
You may use the following in your answer:

- Francis Drake
- the Netherlands.

You **must** also use information of your own. **(12 marks)**

One way to analyse historical events is using a time frame (long-term, short-term). Sometimes it is more appropriate than analysing by political, economic, social and religious (PESR) factors. Historical events and developments are the result of lots of factors building up over time. These factors can be:

- Long-term: ongoing issues, changes, trends or developments – the themes of the era.
- Short-term: specific events that may spring from the long-term issues, trends or developments. Short-term causes help lead directly to the event.

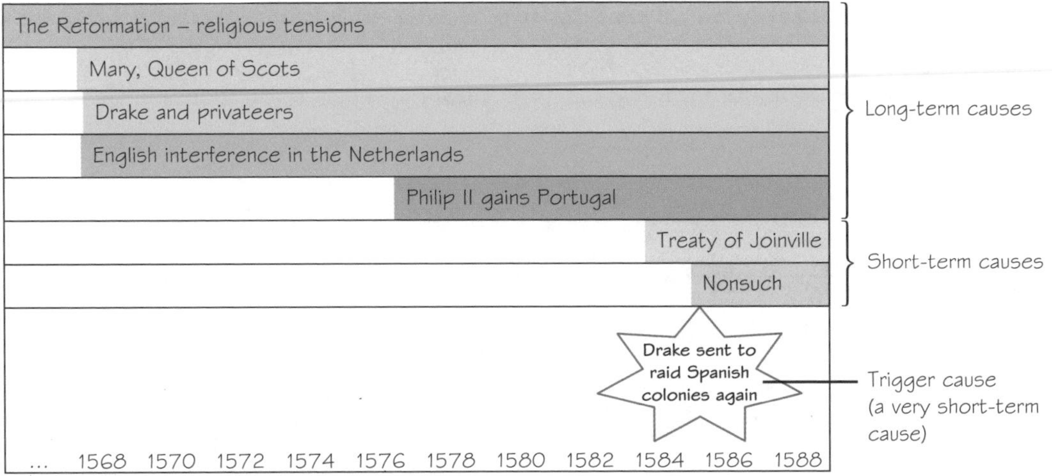

A chronological approach can help you show how one thing led to another. It can help explain why people at the time reacted in the way they did because it shows the order in which they experienced events. It could also be applied after grouping causes into political, economic, social and religious.

The three key questions in the **skills boosts** will help you to use long-term and short-term effectively.

1. **How do I decide what are long-term and short-term causes?**
2. **How do I combine long-term and short-term causes?**
3. **How can I use chronology without telling a narrative?**

Get started

Here is another exam-style question.

Exam-style question

Explain why Elizabeth I sent troops to the Netherlands at the end of 1585.

You may use the following in your answer:

- the Duke of Alençon
- the Treaty of Joinville in 1584.

You **must** also use information of your own. **(12 marks)**

Here are a student's first thoughts on what to include in their answer:

a *Treaty of Joinville 1584*

b *Philip II's forces in Netherlands to stamp out heresy (Protestantism) since 1568*

c *Elizabeth I under threat from Catholics e.g. Ridolfi plot (1571), Throckmorton plot (1583), Jesuits*

d *William of Orange assassinated 1584*

e *Duke of Alençon died 1584*

f *Elizabeth I's strategy to bring Spain to negotiate over the Netherlands wasn't working*

g *Pressure from Privy Council*

h *Treaty of Nonsuch 1585*

i *Mary, Queen of Scots = Catholic alternative to Elizabeth I*

j *Drake's achievements boosted English morale (e.g. circumnavigation)*

1 Identify trends and developments from the list that Elizabeth I had been facing in the long-term.

2 What new developments were there in the run up to Elizabeth I's decision to send troops to the Netherlands at the end of 1585?

3 Is there one change that you think was perhaps more important than any other in Elizabeth I's decision? Which one and why?

Remember this?

Anglo–Spanish relations 1580–1588

This unit uses the theme of Anglo–Spanish relations 1580–1588 to build your skills in analysing within a time frame. If you need to review your knowledge of this theme, work through these pages.

1. Read the following list and circle the one that was **not** one of Elizabeth I's aims:
   - a improving trade
   - b avoiding war
   - c protecting England's borders
   - d deposing King Philip II of Spain.

2. Write the letter for each statement below in the table to show which apply to William of Orange and which apply to the Duke of Alençon. Some of the statements might apply to both men.

A Dutch, Protestant leader
B next in line to the French throne
C fought the Spanish in the Netherlands
D Elizabeth I promised marriage to him
E assassinated in July 1584
F died in June 1584
G French, Catholic noble
H the Dutch turned to Elizabeth I after his death

William of Orange	Duke of Alençon

3. Draw lines linking the correct date to the event.

1580	Throckmorton plot
1581	Treaty of Nonsuch; Leicester sent to the Netherlands with troops to support the Dutch Protestant rebels; Drake raided Spain's New World colonies
1583	Spain acquired Portugal
1584	Deaths of Duke of Alençon and William of Orange. Treaty of Joinville
1585	Spain launched the Armada – it was defeated
1586	Alençon visited England; Elizabeth I gave him £70,000
1587	Babington plot; Leicester accepted title of Governor General of the Netherlands for Elizabeth I
1588	Drake's raid on Cadiz; Leicester returned to England for good after a not very successful campaign

4 Read the following statements and tick to say if they are true or false.

		true	false
a	Drake's attack on Cadiz in 1587 is known as the 'curling of the King of Spain's beard'.		
b	Elizabeth I and Leicester had different aims in the Netherlands: she wanted to liberate them and he wanted to return them to how they had been governed in 1548.		
c	The King of France agreed with the Catholic League's aim of ridding France of Protestantism.		
d	Elizabeth I managed to ally England with France until 1587.		
e	The English had no success in the Netherlands during the 1585–1587 campaign.		
f	Philip II made the decision to send an Armada against England after Mary, Queen of Scots' execution in 1587.		

5 In each of the following lists, circle which is the odd one out, and explain why.

a Earl of Leicester   William of Orange   John Casimir   Duke of Alba

....

b Duke of Parma   Duke of Alençon   Don Juan   Duke of Alba

....

c Portugal   Mexico   Peru   Chile

....

d Launch of the Armada   execution of Mary, Queen of Scots   singeing of the King of Spain's beard   Leicester returning from the Netherlands for good

....

e Francis Drake   Robert Dudley   John Hawkins   William Stanley

....

6 Link up each sentence starter with an appropriate ending.

A In 1584 Elizabeth I and Cecil preferred a cautious approach to the Netherlands	a but returned to France in 1583 having failed to defeat them.
B One achievement of the Earl of Leicester in the Netherlands was that	b Sir William Stanley and Rowland York defected to the Spanish in the Netherlands.
C The Dutch Protestants found it hard to trust Leicester and the English after	c the French Catholic League and Spain.
D Alençon returned to the Netherlands to fight the Spanish in 1582	d but other members of the Privy Council urged direct intervention.
E The Treaty of Joinville was signed in 1584 between	e the Duke of Parma was unable to capture the deep-water port of Ostend.

How do I decide what are long-term and short-term causes?

History can be analysed by identifying long-term causes and short-term causes of events.

① Read the following list and tick ✓ whether you think they are long-term or short-term causes for Philip II's decision to prepare an Armada.

	Causes of Philip II's decision to prepare the Armada	Short-term	Long-term
A	1579 England getting more involved in Netherlands (e.g. Casimir 1578–1579; support for Alençon 1581–1582)		
B	English privateers raiding Spain's New World colonies = problem since 1560s		
C	Elizabeth I's involvement in Netherlands = problem since 1567 (e.g. Genoese Loan 1568; Pacification of Ghent 1576)		
D	Elizabeth I taking harsher actions against Catholics since 1581		
E	Attempts to replace Protestant Elizabeth I with Catholic Mary, Queen of Scots failed (1571 Ridolfi, 1583–1584 Throckmorton; Catholic priests travelled to England from 1574)		
F	Religious tensions – Reformation in Europe and England – Philip II fighting against heresy in Netherlands since 1566		
G	Treaty of Joinville – Spain allied with France 1584		
H	Drake was sent to raid Spain's New World settlements, disrupt flow of resources to Spain 1585		
I	Treaty of Nonsuch 1585 led to England directly helping Dutch Protestant rebels		
J	Drake's circumnavigation of globe completed in 1580; he took £400,000 from Spanish ships and colonies and was knighted		

Lots of the problems in the table, such as those to do with the Dutch revolt in the Netherlands, had been going on for a long time, so why did Philip II make the decision in 1585?

② What might have been the **trigger events** that finally persuaded him to prepare the Armada and why? ✎

 How do I combine long-term and short-term causes?

A good way to organise your essay is to divide it into sections on different long-term causes. Then you can look at how short-term causes combined with them to cause the event in question.

The chart below shows three long-term causes from the chart on page 55.

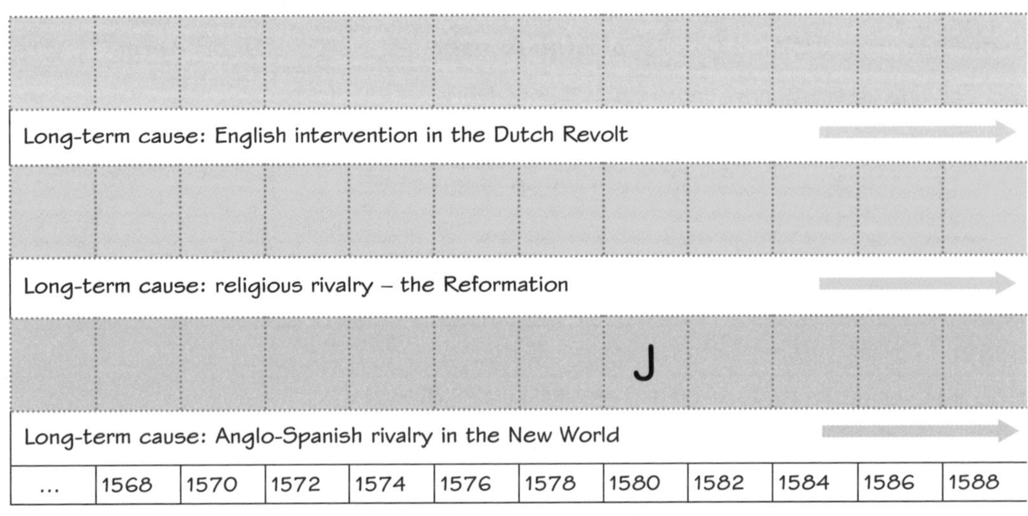

1. Look at the short-term causes on your chart on page 55. Plot them on the chart above to show how they related to the long-term causes. Event J has already been done for you.

Apparently, it was Drake's attacks on Spanish colonies (on Elizabeth I's orders) in 1585 that finally led Philip II to decide upon the Armada. Drake had often attacked Spain's colonies before, so why was this time different?

2. Which other short-term events do you think had the most impact on Philip II's decision to build an Armada to invade England? What made him react differently to Drake's raid in 1585? Pick three and briefly explain your choices.

Think like Philip: the Armada was an expensive, risky venture.

3 How can I use chronology without telling a narrative?

The key to using chronology to analyse events is to show how things **combined** and evaluate their **impact**. This skills booster will help you to use chronology to analyse events.

Read through the two student extracts below looking at why Philip II built the Armada. One is a narrative account. This means it simply tells us what happened. The other analyses causes of declining relations. This means it looks at the type of causes and how they contributed to the decline.

1 a Tick which extract is the analysis?

Extract A ☐

By the end of 1585 Philip II had decided to invade England. Anglo-Spanish rivalry in the New World was a long-term cause. Drake had attacked Spanish colonies in 1572, 1577–1580 and 1585. Elizabeth I had supported him. In 1585 she signed the Treaty of Nonsuch. Before then, in 1584, Spain had signed the Treaty of Joinville with France. Philip II also got Portugal's navy and wealth in 1580.

Extract B ☐

Philip II decided to invade England in 1585 after Drake's raid on Spanish New World colonies. This, on top of all his other raids (e.g. 1572, 1577–1580) greatly worsened long-term Anglo-Spanish relations. Philip II's decision coincided with Elizabeth I helping Dutch rebels under the Treaty of Nonsuch. The Netherlands was a long-term problem but by 1585 Spain had Portugal's resources and had made an alliance with France in 1584. All these factors combined to make Philip prepare an Armada.

b Highlight the words in the analysis that show a combination of causes working together.

c Highlight in a different colour the words that measure the impact of the different causes.

Useful words to combine causes and consequences	Useful words to analyse impact
strengthened / reinforced / combined came together / coincided on top of / added to / followed by / following on from	worsened / exacerbated / declined reduced / improved / increased accelerated

2 Fill in the gaps in the following paragraph to show how causes combined and contributed to the decline in Anglo-Spanish relations. Use the words in the box. Write the letters in the spaces.

By 1585, Anglo-Spanish relations had been in .... decline for many years. In the .... this decline was .... by Elizabeth I's support for Francis Drake's attacks on Spanish colonies (e.g. 1577–1580 and 1585). .... the 1585 Treaty of Nonsuch, when England agreed to support Dutch rebels, Philip II decided to act against Elizabeth. .... improved relations with France under the Treaty of Joinville in 1584, ... Spain's wealth increasing after it got Portugal in 1580, ... factors .... long-term issues to convince Philip to build the Armada against England.

A added to	B combined with	C coming on top of	D long-term
E made much worse	F at the same time	G short-term	H short-term

Sample response

Look at the student's notes for the exam-style question below.

Exam-style question

Explain why Anglo–Spanish relations declined 1580–1588?
You may use the following in your answer:

- Francis Drake
- the Netherlands.

You **must** also use information of your own. **(12 marks)**

a *Armada 1588!*

b *1580 Elizabeth I knighted Drake after circumnavigation + raids on Spanish colonies (took £400,000) = Phillip II angry*

c *Treaty of Nonsuch 1585 – Elizabeth I directly involved in Netherlands*

d *Elizabeth I = Protestant, Phillip II = Catholic and aimed to stamp out heresy*

e *Singeing of the King of Spain's beard 1587 (Drake again!)*

f *English troops sent to Netherlands from end 1585 (help Dutch Protestant rebels against Phillip II)*

g *Philip II supporting Mary, Queen of Scots – Catholic rival to Elizabeth I (Throckmorton 1583, Babington 1586)*

h *Elizabeth I supported Dutch rebels indirectly too – Alençon given £70,000 in 1581*

i *Philip II decide on Armada after Drake's 1585 raids*

j *Philip II & France allies, Joinville Treaty 1584 – both Catholic countries = danger to Protestant England*

The student decides to organise their answer into three long-term causes: the rebellion in the Netherlands; the New World; and religion.

1 Write one sentence about each of the long-term causes to explain why it led to a decline in Anglo-Spanish relations.

....

....

....

2 Put the causes in the list above into chronological order, under one of the long-term causes below.

Rebellion in the Netherlands	The New World	Religion

Your turn!

Exam-style question

Explain why Anglo–Spanish relations declined 1580–1588?
You may use the following in your answer:

- Francis Drake
- the Netherlands.

You **must** also use information of your own. **(12 marks)**

Pick one of the long-term causes you have looked at on page 58 and write up that section of the essay. Try to use the words from page 57 to help show how short-term and long-term causes combined.

Review your skills

Check up

Review your response to the exam-style question on page 59. Tick ✓ the column to show how well you think you have done each of the following.

	Had a go ✓	Nearly there ✓	Got it! ✓
identified long-term and short-term causes	☐	☐	☐
shown how long-term and short-term causes combine	☐	☐	☐
given an analysis rather than a narrative account	☐	☐	☐

Look over all of your work in this chapter. Note down three things you have learned that you will do when you have to answer a question that asks you to explain something.

1. ....
2. ....
3. ....

Need more practice?

On a separate piece of paper, plan and write your response to the exam-style question below.

Exam-style question

Explain why Elizabeth I faced challenges to her religious settlement 1558–1569.

You may use the following in your answer:

- vestments
- Mary, Queen of Scots.

You **must** also include information of your own. **(12 marks)**

How confident do you feel about each of these **skills**? Colour in the bars.

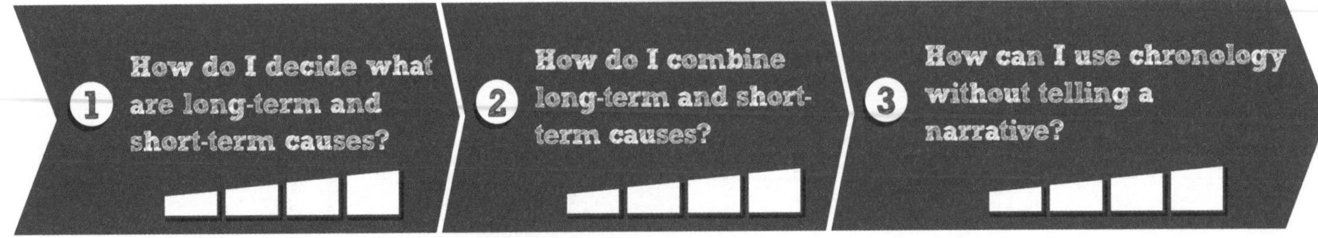

1 How do I decide what are long-term and short-term causes?
2 How do I combine long-term and short-term causes?
3 How can I use chronology without telling a narrative?

7 Analysis by significance

One way to analyse history is to identify the most important causes and consequences. This unit will help you develop the skills to decide how **significant** different causes and consequences are. The skills you will build are to:

- decide the relative significance of different causes and consequences
- identify the most significant cause or consequence
- use significance to organise an answer.

In the exam, you will be asked to tackle questions like the one below. This unit will prepare you to write your own response to this type of question.

Exam-style question

'Native American resistance was to blame for the failure of the Virginia colonies 1585–1588.'
How far do you agree? Explain your answer.

You may use the following in your answer:

- the voyage to Virginia
- Wingina.

You **must** also use information of your own. **(16 marks)**

Causes or consequences can be ranked using pyramid-type diagrams.

Diagram 1

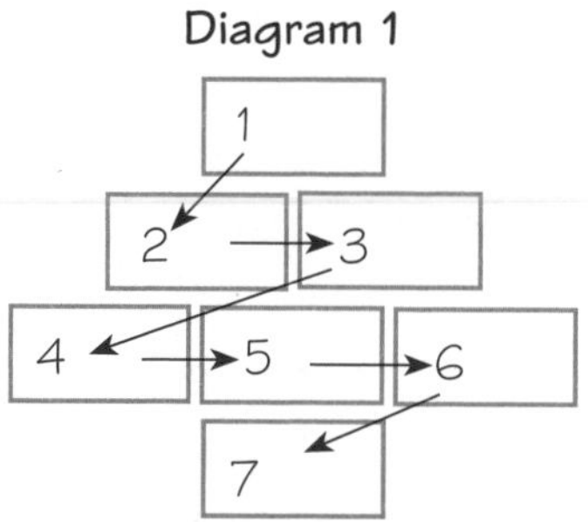

Causes or consequences numbered from most to least important.

Diagram 2

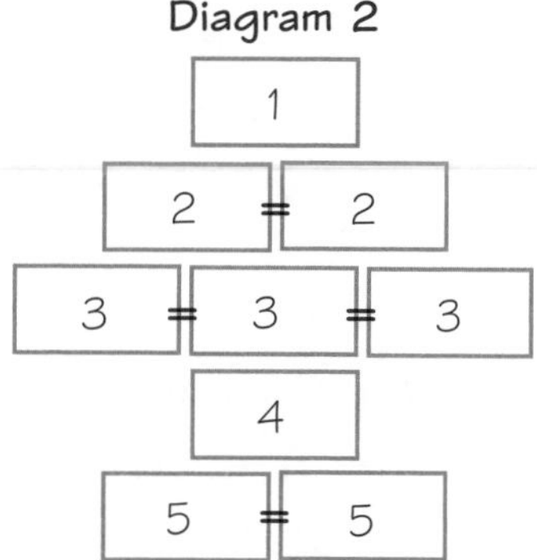

Causes or consequences can be equally important and some are given a similar level of importance.

To decide **how important** something is, look at the **impact** of the cause, consequence or change. An important event might have a big impact on what happens next and might be a point of no return when things cannot go back to the way they were.

The three key questions in the **skills boosts** will help you to answer a question asking you to analyse the significance of causes and consequences.

1. How do I decide relative significance of causes and consequences?
2. How do I identify what is most significant?
3. How can I use significance to organise an answer?

Get started

Look at these two exam-style questions then read the evidence A–I.

Exam-style question

1 Explain why the Elizabethans colonised Virginia. You may use the following in your answer:

- improvements in ships
- wealth.

You **must** also use information of your own. **(12 marks)**

Exam-style question

2 Explain why the Elizabethans undertook voyages of discovery. You may use the following in your answer:

- improvements in ships
- wealth.

You **must** also use information of your own. **(12 marks)**

A Improved navigation and maps made long journeys easier.

B Trade. There was silver, tobacco, sugar and other valuable resources.

C Elizabeth I sponsored and encouraged ventures in the New World.

D New galleons could carry larger cargoes and more supplies.

E Initial contacts between the English and Native Americans were very friendly.

F Anglo–Spanish rivalry. England needed more resources and to disrupt Spain's supplies.

G Newer galleons had better firepower to defend against, and attack, Spanish ships.

H English bases in North America would be useful for attacking Spanish New World colonies.

I Wealth. Drake, for example, returned from the New World very rich. This encouraged others.

1. Decide which piece of evidence would be useful in an answer to each of the exam-style questions. Are there any pieces of evidence that would be useful for both questions? Complete the table below, inserting the evidence letter in the appropriate column.

Question 1	Both questions	Question 2

2. Choose one of the pieces of evidence that could be used for either question. If you were answering exam-style question 2, explain why that evidence is more or less important for your essay than an essay answering exam-style question 1.

Remember this?

Exploration and voyages of discovery

This unit uses the theme of exploration and voyages of discovery in Elizabethan England to build your skills in using significance to write an effective answer. If you need to review your knowledge of this theme, work through these pages.

1. Look at these multiple-choice questions about Drake's circumnavigation of the globe. Tick the correct answers.

a How much treasure did Drake bring back?

- i £400,000
- ii £28,000
- iii £150,000
- iv £12,000

b How many ships did Drake return with?

- i None
- ii One
- iii Two
- iv Three

c What territory did Drake claim for England?

- i California
- ii San Juan de Ulúa
- iii Virginia
- iv Nova Albion

d Which were consequences of Drake's circumnavigation?

- i Further exploration of America
- ii Angered Philip II of Spain
- iii Boosted English morale
- iv Colonisation of America

2. **a** Drake, Hawkins and Raleigh all led voyages of discovery. Draw lines to link each voyage with its significant consequence.

Date of voyage	Significant consequence
A 1562	a Circumnavigation of the globe
B 1567–1568	b Conflict with Spain at San Juan de Ulúa, Mexico
C 1571–1572	c Elizabeth I invested in this voyage to Panama, which captured £40,000 of Spanish treasure
D 1577–1580	d Fact-finding mission to Virginia
E 1584	e First group of colonists sent to Virginia
F 1585	f First trans-Atlantic Triangular Trade expedition
G 1587	g Second group of colonists to Virginia

b Write the letters of the voyages under the correct explorer in the table.

	Drake	Hawkins	Raleigh
Voyages			

3. Read the following statements about the first attempt to colonise Virginia. Tick ✓ to show which ones are true and which are false.

		true	false
a	Raleigh led the expeditions to colonise Virginia.		
b	The colonists worked well together to build a strong, stone fort at Roanoke.		
c	The colonists did not arrive in time to plant crops for the winter.		
d	The colonists did not have enough supplies or seeds to plant to survive the winter.		
e	Manteo and Wanchese led the Native Americans of Roanoke.		
f	The Native Americans where the colonists settled were Algonquians.		
g	The colonists were willing to live and work among the Algonquians.		

4. Give ✎ one way in which the colonists who were part of the second attempt to colonise Virginia were different from those involved in the first.

....

5. Write down ✎ the names of the two leaders of the first two colonies at Roanoke (1585–1586 and 1587–1590).

....

6. Read the events described in the boxes below. Add a number ✎ from 1 to 12 to show the order in which they happened.

A ☐ Raleigh made Manteo leader of the Virginia colony and John White expedition leader.

B ☐ The colonists made more and more demands on the Algonquians.

C Manteo attacked friendly Croatoan Indians by mistake. ☐

D ☐ All supplies on the *Tiger* were ruined and the colonists arrived too late to plant anything.

E ☐ Five ships left England for Virginia.

F ☐ Thomas Harriot wrote an English–Algonquian dictionary.

G ☐ Ralph Lane led the surviving colonists back to England.

H ☐ A second group of colonists left for Virginia.

I ☐ George Howe was murdered by Roanoke Indians.

J ☐ Manteo and Wanchese arrived in England.

K ☐ White left for England. When he returned to Virginia, the colonists. had disappeared.

L ☐ Wingina asked other chiefs to help him attack the colonists.

1 How do I decide relative significance of causes and consequences?

Once you have gathered your evidence, it is important to think about the impact of different causes, consequences or changes **and** look at the question you are answering. This skills boost will help you to do this.

Think about the question of who had the greater impact on Elizabethan England: Drake or Raleigh? One way of doing this is to ask yourself the following question for each person:

? What difference would it have made to Elizabethan England if he had not been there?

1. Study the evidence listed in the table below. Think about the **consequences** of each man's actions.

Sir Francis Drake	Sir Walter Raleigh
1 Traded across the Atlantic, making himself and his backers, including Elizabeth I, very rich.	1 Suppressed rebellions in Ireland in 1580.
2 1577–1580: Circumnavigated the world while attacking Spanish ships and colonies, capturing £400,000 of treasure.	2 Sent exploratory expedition to North America 1584.
3 1585: sent by Elizabeth I to attack Spanish colonies and ships in the New World.	3 Planned and sponsored the first English colonies in Virginia in 1585. He raised the funds, ships and settlers. Virginia was vital for new resources, and as a base from which to attack Spain's New World colonies.
4 1587: raided Cadiz, disrupting Philip II's Armada preparation, buying England time to prepare.	4 Organised second colony in Virginia.
5 Vice admiral of the navy that fought against the Spanish Armada.	5 Popularised tobacco at court.

a After reading the evidence in the table, who do you think had the greater impact on Elizabethan England?

....

b Which piece of evidence convinced you the most?

....

c Why?

....

....

2. Study the evidence again, and ask yourself a different question.

? Who had the greater impact on the development of the future British Empire?

a Decide who you think had the greater impact now.

....

b Which piece of evidence convinced you?

....

c Why?

....

....

2 How do I identify what is most significant?

One way of working out how important a cause was is to look at its links to other causes that happened afterwards. This skills boost will help you to do this.

Here is a list of causes of the failure of the first Virginia colony:

A	The colonists left England too late to plant crops to harvest for the winter.
B	Vital supplies of seeds, food and gunpowder were lost when the *Tiger* ran aground.
C	The colonists did not have the right mix of skills to tackle the challenges of a new colony.
D	The English were dependent on the Native Americans for help and food.
E	Although welcoming at first, the Native Americans turned against the English.
F	Chief Wingina, who ruled the region, was unpredictable and did not trust the colonists.
G	The English brought diseases that killed many Algonquians, turning them against the colonists.

1 a Start with cause A. Read the other causes and decide whether any of them were caused by cause A. Write the letter of the cause/problem.

....

b Start with cause F. What problem did cause F cause?

....

2 Choose another cause from the list. What was its impact? What other causes/problems did it lead to?

....

3 a Rank causes (problems) A, F and your own choice in order of importance (1 being the most important) in explaining why the Virginia colony failed.

A [ ] F [ ] .... [ ]

b Explain your decision.

....

....

....

....

3 How can I use significance to organise an answer?

Exam-style question

'The most important consequence of Drake's circumnavigation was increased tensions with Spain.' How far do you agree? **(16 marks)**

You will need to decide how significant the consequences of Drake's voyage were if you are to judge how far you agree that increased tensions with Spain was most important.

Some consequences are long-term – they develop into trends, or bring about changes for years to come.

Some are short-term – these effects don't last long, but can be dramatic.

Consequences of circumnavigation	Long- or short-term?
A Elizabeth I knighted Drake on his return to England	
B England's reputation as a sea-faring nation was boosted	
C Drake's logs contained a great deal of information about North America	
D Nova Albion was claimed for England	
E Encouraged English exploration, and colonisation, of Americas	
F Drake attacked more Spanish New World colonies on the Pacific coast	
G £400,000 of treasure was taken from Spain for Drake's investors	
H Philip II angered by the actions of both Drake and Elizabeth I	
I Four ships and many lives were lost	
J There was a huge boost to England's morale	

One way to decide about which consequences are more significant is to consider how widely, and for how long, their impact is felt.

1. Decide whether the consequences above are long- or short-term. Write 'long' or 'short' in the table.

Another way to decide which consequences are more significant is to think about how they link together.

2. a. Write which consequences link to H? ....

   b. Write which link to E? ....

3. Which consequence of Drake's circumnavigation do you think was most significant and why?

....

4. Study the evidence above and complete the pyramid diagram by ranking consequences according to their impact. Remember, the pyramid can show that some consequences are equally important. (see page 61)

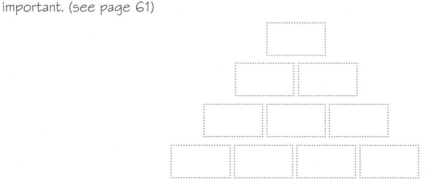

Sample response

When deciding what you need to write about for a history essay, deciding the order of importance (impact and significance) is a really effective approach. You are going to use this method on the exam-style question below.

Exam-style question

'Native American resistance was to blame for the failure of the Virginia colonies 1585–1588.' How far do you agree? Explain your answer.

You may use the following in your answer:

- the voyage to Virginia
- Wingina.

You **must** also use information of your own. **(16 marks)**

Look at these pieces of evidence that a student has compiled to answer this exam-style question:

A *The colonists left England too late to plant crops to harvest for the winter (voyage).*

B *Vital supplies of seeds, food and gunpowder were lost when the 'Tiger' ran aground (voyage).*

C *The colonists did not have the right mix of skills.*

D *The English were very dependent on the Native Americans for help and food to survive.*

E *Wingina believed the English had supernatural powers from their god to use against the Native Americans.*

F *Wingina, who ruled the region, was unpredictable and did not trust the colonists.*

G *The English brought diseases that killed many Algonquians, turning them against the colonists.*

H *Lane led an attack against the Algonquians after discovering that Wingina planned to ambush them.*

1. The student is planning to use this evidence under the following four **factor** headings, in this order:

   1 Native American resistance: ....

   2 The colonists: ....

   3 Poor planning: ....

   4 Luck: ....

   a. List which pieces of evidence **A–H** could be used for each heading in order of importance.

   b. Highlight in different colours the evidence that links to the question focus of Native American resistance and to the prompts in the question – the voyage to Virginia and Wingina.

2. Explain which single **cause** you think was the most important and why.

   ....

   ....

   ....

3. Write down which **factor** you think was the most important and why.

   ....

   ....

   ....

Your turn!

You are now going to plan and write your response to this exam-style question.

Exam-style question

'Inexperience was the most important reason for the failure of the Virginia colonies 1585–1588.'
How far do you agree? Explain your answer.
You may use the following in your answer:

- the colonists
- Wingina.

You **must** also use information of your own. **(16 marks)**

1. Study the pieces of evidence (**A–J**) below. Highlight in different colours anything that links to the question focus of inexperience, and to the prompts in the question – the colonists and Wingina.

2. Use the space alongside the evidence to draw a pyramid plan to answer the question using the evidence provided.

A *1584: Raleigh sent a fact-finding expedition to Virginia.*

B *This was the first expedition to establish a colony and so no one had any previous experience.*

C *The expedition leader, Grenville, and governor of Virginia, Lane, did not get on.*

D *The colonists left England too late to plant crops to harvest for the winter.*

E *Vital supplies of seeds, food and gunpowder were lost when the 'Tiger' ran aground.*

F *The colonists did not have the right mix of skills and were not used to hardship.*

G *The colonists were very dependent on the Native Americans for help and food to survive.*

H *Wingina, who ruled the region, was unpredictable and did not trust the colonists.*

I *The English brought diseases that killed many Algonquians, turning them against the colonists.*

J *The colonists twice led attacks against the Native Americans, in 1586 and 1587.*

3. Note down which single cause you think was the most important (had the greatest impact) for explaining the failure of the colony and explain why.

....

....

....

4. Circle the word or phrase below that you think best shows **how far** inexperience was the most important cause of the failure of the colonies in Virginia 1585–1588.

Totally	Largely	Mainly	Not really	Not at all

Review your skills

Check up

Review your response to the exam-style question on page 69. Tick the column to show how well you think you have done each of the following.

	Had a go	Nearly there	Got it!
decided relative significance of causes and consequence	☐	☐	☐
decided what is most significant	☐	☐	☐
used significance to organise an answer	☐	☐	☐

Look over all of your work in this unit. Note down three things you have learned that you will do when you have to answer a question that asks you to analyse the significance of causes, consequences or changes.

1. ....
2. ....
3. ....

Need more practice?

On a separate piece of paper, plan and write your response to the exam-style question below.

Exam-style question

'Seeking wealth was the most important reason for Elizabethan voyages of discovery.'

How far do you agree. Explain your answer.

You may use the following in your answer:

- Sir Francis Drake's circumnavigation of the globe
- Spain.

You **must** also use information of your own. **(16 marks)**

How confident do you feel about each of these **skills**? Colour in the bars.

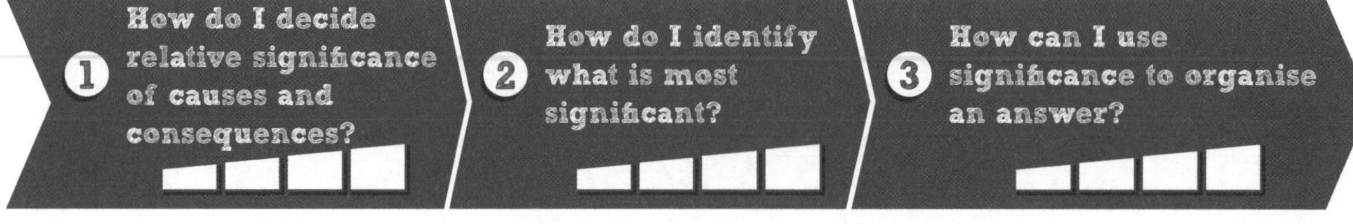

1 How do I decide relative significance of causes and consequences?
2 How do I identify what is most significant?
3 How can I use significance to organise an answer?

8 Conclusions

Conclusions are important. They are the last chance for you to convince the reader that your explanations and reasoning have merit. The skills you will build in this unit will help you to:

- recognise what a good conclusion looks like
- understand how to write an effective conclusion
- understand why it is important to know the conclusion before the essay is written.

Here is an example of an exam-style question that you may encounter that asks you to come to a conclusion.

Exam-style question

'Sheep farming was the most important cause of poverty in Elizabethan England.'

How far do you agree? Explain your answer.

You may use the following in your answer:

- enclosure
- price rises.

You **must** also use information of your own. **(16 marks)**

Lawyers make closing arguments to convince the jury of the case they have made in court. When you write a history essay you are presenting your argument on the issue in the question to the reader. Your conclusion should persuade the reader that the case you have presented works well.

Here are some useful words and phrases to help you write a conclusion that does all the right things.

To start / end your conclusion:

- 'To summarise ...'
- 'Overall ...'
- 'All in all ...'
- 'In conclusion ...'

To pull out the most important point from your answer:

- 'The most important point / factor ...'

To compare the factor in the question with other important factors:

- 'Perhaps more important, however ...'
- 'However, x was not as important as y ...'
- 'On the other hand ...'

The three key questions in the **skills boosts** will help you to write conclusions effectively.

What does a good conclusion look like?

What goes into an effective conclusion?

How do I construct an effective conclusion?

Get started

Here are notes made by a student planning an answer to the exam-style question on page 71.

POVERTY: WHY?

Population growth = more demand for: food, jobs, land = food prices up, wages down, rents up; population grew up to 35%; London grew very fast = 150,000 in 1603 = 10x bigger than Norwich

Unemployment = important other factor – trade slumps and also more people = more workers; 1572 Vagabonds Act recognised unemployment as a specific problem – not just laziness

Sheep farming? Profits up because prices up because demand up because of population growth

Sheep farming → enclosure → merging some small farms, evicting tenant farmers; enclosing common land → problems because it was vital for poor to forage (firewood etc.) and graze pigs. But although lots of angry pamphlets condemned enclosure only 2–3% of land enclosed.

Below is the conclusion to the essay the student wrote using these notes.

Student A

It cannot be said that the most important reason for poverty in Elizabethan England was sheep farming. Population growth had a far bigger impact because it forced up prices for everything, including food and rent. However, population growth did make sheep farming more profitable and so there was some enclosure, which contributed to poverty. Other important causes of poverty included age, gender, illness and disability. Although sheep farming played a part, unemployment was more important, and population growth the most important reason of all.

1. Tick the items on the conclusion checklist below that you think the student has done well.
2. Write a sentence to explain how effective you think the conclusion is.

....

....

....

....

....

....

Conclusion checklist	✓
Gives overall summary of the key points of the essay	
Gives a clear, supported judgement	
Answers the question directly – uses question wording	
No surprises – doesn't suddenly bring in any new information	

The problem of the poor

This unit uses the theme of poverty in Elizabethan England to develop your conclusion writing skills. If you need to review your knowledge of this theme, work through these pages.

1. This table shows a list of seven social groups. Which of them were more likely to be poor and which less likely? Tick the correct box for each social group.

	more likely	less likely
households headed by working, adult males		
households headed by working, adult females		
those younger than 16 years old		
16 to 60-year-olds		
those over 60 years old		
people with disabilities or illnesses		
skilled workers		

2. Statements A to D below are all steps leading from sheep farming becoming more profitable to an increase in vagrancy. Write the correct letter in each blank box of the diagram below to show how one led to the other.

A There was rural depopulation as people left the land in search of work.

B There was an increase in enclosure to provide grazing for sheep.

C Some tenant farmers were evicted, common land was taken and less labour was needed to farm sheep.

D Rural unemployment and poverty increased.

Sheep farming became profitable. → [ ] → [ ] → [ ] → [ ] → There was an increase in vagrancy.

3. Cross out ~~cat~~ any of the following that were **not** a consequence of population growth.

a increased food prices

b unemployment increased

c wages reduced

d the death rate rose

e rent prices increased

4. Explain what common land was, and why it was important to people in the countryside.

....

....

....

5 Explain the difference between poor relief and the poor rate.

....

....

....

6 Read the following statements about poverty in Elizabethan times and tick to say if they are true or false.

	Statement	true	false
a	The idle (undeserving) poor were treated more harshly than the impotent (deserving) poor.	☐	☐
b	A vagrant, or vagabond, was someone without a home who wandered the country begging.	☐	☐
c	Unemployment fell when there was a downturn in the cloth trade.	☐	☐
d	Vagrants would be thrown in gaol.	☐	☐
e	All Elizabethans thought unemployment was simply caused by laziness.	☐	☐
f	Ipswich had a school for poor children and a hospital for the poor and sick.	☐	☐
g	Officials often gave vagrants money and sent them on their way rather than arrest them.	☐	☐

7 Draw lines linking each impact (a–f) to its relevant Act of Parliament.

a Established national poor rate for the first time.

b Those who refused work were sent to a house of correction.

c JPs were to keep a register of the poor.

d Anyone who refused to pay poor rates could be imprisoned.

e Towns and cities had to find work for the able bodied poor.

f Set increasingly harsh punishments for those found guilty of vagrancy – the third time led to the death penalty.

1563 Statute of Artificers

1572 Vagabonds Act

1576 Poor Relief Act

8 Link up the answer on the right to the questions on the left.

A What was the connection between Anglo–Spanish relations and poverty?

B How much land in England was actually enclosed?

C How many vagrants were whipped?

D How much bigger than Norwich, England's second city, was London?

E Why was the 1572 Vagabonds Act a turning point in poor relief?

a Ten times

b Because it introduced a national poor rate.

c Trade was disrupted.

d 2–3%

e less than 10%

1 What does a good conclusion look like?

A good conclusion should answer the essay question directly by giving a clear summary of the key points in the essay and the judgement made.

Look again at the student's conclusion on page 72 (Student A). Then compare it with the version below written by another student – Student B.

Student B

The most important reason for poverty in Elizabethan England was population growth, which was up to 35%. This forced up prices for everything, including food and rent. Sheep farming became more profitable because of population growth and there was some enclosure, which caused poverty, but only 2–3% of land was affected. Unemployment, on the other hand, was a much bigger problem as is shown by it being recognised for the first time in the Vagabonds Act of 1572. For these reasons, sheep farming was not the most important reason for poverty in Elizabethan England. Although it played a part, unemployment was more important, and population growth was the most important reason of all.

1 **a** Answer the questions in the following table for each version by writing Yes or No in the box.

Does the conclusion...	Student A	Student B
answer the question directly, using the question wording?		
give an overall summary of the key points of the essay?		
give a clear judgement about how far sheep farming was the most important reason for poverty?		
provide supporting information for its key points?		

b Highlight where Student B gives a clear judgement about whether sheep farming was the most important reason for poverty in Elizabethan England.

c Write a sentence explaining why Student B's conclusion is effective.

....

....

2 To improve your conclusion, don't forget to use words that can guide the reader through your answer. Use some of the useful words and phrases shown in the word box and words and phrases of your own to write in the gaps in the paragraph below.

in conclusion   overall / all in all   therefore   on the other hand   not as important a factor   the most important   perhaps more important   furthermore

.... population growth was .... reason for poverty in Elizabethan England. .... sheep farming was .... because only 2–3% of land was enclosed. Also unemployment was .... than sheep farming too, because it was included in the 1572 Vagabonds Act. ...., population growth was most important because it contributed to all the other causes.

2 What goes into an effective conclusion?

Different questions will need different types of conclusions. This skills boost will help you to identify what key aspects are needed for an effective conclusion.

A student was answering the following question:

Exam-style question

'Unemployment was the most important cause of poverty in Elizabethan England.'
How far do you agree? Explain your answer.

The student decided that population growth was the most important reason.

1. Look back at the example of conclusions on pages 72 and 75 and the useful words and phrases on pages 71 and 75. Write the opening sentence for the conclusion.

2. Look at the following sentences. They could all be used to complete the conclusion you have started, although they are not in the right order.

A	It grew 35%, causing rises in prices and rents but a fall in wages, all of which increased poverty.
B	Unemployment was recognised as an important problem in the Vagabonds Act (1572).
C	Perhaps more important than unemployment, however, was population growth.
D	Unemployment also made poverty even worse when there were trade slumps like 1568–1573.
E	The more people there were, the more unemployment there was, too.

a. Which sentences give a clear judgement about how important unemployment was relative to other factors?

b. Which sentences give specific evidence used to show how important unemployment was?

c. Highlight the words that show population growth was more important than unemployment.

d. Which sentence gives specific evidence to show how important population growth was?

3. Write the final sentence of the conclusion. You can look back at other examples to help you.

3 How do I construct an effective conclusion?

An effective conclusion is well constructed.

A student had considered how far they agreed with the statement in the following exam-style question. Look at their plan.

Exam-style question

'Enclosure was the most important reason for the increase in vagabondage in Elizabethan England.'

Population growth	*Unemployment*	*Enclosure*
– *35% increase* – *Pushed up prices and rents → poverty* – *More vagrancy as too many people not enough jobs* – *Led to increased demand for sheep farming (wool, meat)*	– *Unemployment → vagrancy. People left their homes to look for work* – *Trade slumps → unemployment, e.g. 1568–1573, and 1586–1588* – *Unemployment so serious it was recognised in Vagabonds Act 1572* – *Enclosure and rural unemployment*	– *Enclosure → tenants losing farms* – *Enclosure → fewer labourers needed* – *BUT Enclosure affected only 2–3% of land, THOUGH seen as important at the time*

They then concluded from their plan that:

- *Population growth was the most important reason for vagrancy.*
- *The question focus, enclosure, was not as important as unemployment as a reason for the increase in vagabondage.*

Remember, a fully developed conclusion should contain:

- an opening sentence that answers the question directly
- a sentence (or two) of brief, supported explanation of why x was the most important reason
- a sentence (or two) that **compares** the importance of x with other factors, again with support
- one sentence that reinforces your final judgement.

Make sure that you have included the question focus in your answer.

1 Use the details in the box above **and** the useful words and phrases on pages 71 and 75 to write the student's conclusion using the prompts below.

(First, the opening sentence.)

....

....

(Now, why was population growth the most important factor?)

....

....

....

(And why was it more important than the question focus, enclosure?)

....

....

....

(The final sentence to reinforce the judgement.)

....

....

....

Sample response

Here is a student's plan, introduction and conclusion to the following exam-style question.

Exam-style question

'Enclosure was the most important reason for the increase in vagabonds in Elizabethan England?' How far do you agree? **(16 marks)**

What has the student done well, and what needs improving?

Introductions ought to set out what your answer is going to say and should match your conclusion.

Most important = (1) population growth (2) unemployment, (3) enclosure / sheep farming

*(1) **Population growth** = 35% → prices up, rents up, wages down → poverty, homelessness – couldn't afford rents → evicted or left homes/parishes looking for work, begging – work in towns; e.g. London grew 10X size Norwich. Population growth links to unemployment – combine → make vagrancy worse – more people than jobs sometimes*

*(2) **Unemployment** = increased because of population growth AND trade slumps – cloth trade; slumps → people begging, wandering looking for work – heading to towns e.g. Norwich – a survey in 1570 counted lots of poor people living there who had come from other places*

*(3) **Enclosure** – blamed at time by pamphlets – enclosure for sheep farming – profitable; rural labourers not needed for sheep farming – rural unemployment → vagabonds. Enclosure only 2–3% land. Also crops grown to feed sheep not people*

Vagabondage increased in Elizabethan England. It became a serious problem that worried many people.

In conclusion, population growth was the most important cause of the increase in vagabondage because it led to poverty and homelessness. Many people were therefore forced to leave their homes and beg. Anglo-Spanish relations made things worse because they led to trade slumps. Furthermore this was especially a problem in the countryside because of sheep farming. Overall, however, population growth underpinned all the other problems.

1. Use the conclusion checklist from page 72 to help you. What has the student done / not done in their conclusion?

2. What one change would you make to the conclusion to improve it?

3. What advice would you give the student about the introduction?

Your turn!

Exam-style question

'Elizabethan poor laws significantly improved the lives of the poor.'

How far do you agree? Explain your answer.

You may use the following in your answer:

- 1572 Vagabonds Act
- unemployment.

You **must** also use information of your own. **(16 marks)**

Yes	No
1572 Vagabonds Act – national poor rate; recognised unemployment for the FIRST TIME – towns expected to find work for unemployed 1576 Poor Relief Act developed help for unemployed – JPs to provide raw materials Poor rate / relief taken seriously; not paying rate = prison; not organising relief = fine	Vagabonds Act – punishments for vagrants = whipping, then prison, then death! 1576 Poor Relief Act sent those refusing to work to special prison – house of correction Some improvements not due to poor laws: e.g. Ipswich 1569 school and hospital; local records show less than 10% vagrants whipped; Elizabethans included unemployed as deserving poor for first time Unemployment continued to be a big problem – poor laws did nothing to reduce the causes of poverty.

1. Read the exam-style question and the student's notes above. Plan and then write a conclusion to their essay.

Review your skills

Check up

Review your response to the exam-style question on page 79. Tick ✓ the column to show how well you think you have done each of the following.

	Had a go ✓	Nearly there ✓	Got it! ✓
the conclusion uses the question wording	☐	☐	☐
the conclusion gives a clear judgement	☐	☐	☐
the conclusion summarises the most important points	☐	☐	☐
the introduction matches the conclusion	☐	☐	☐

Look over all of your work in this chapter. Note down three things you have learned that you will do when you have to answer a question that asks you how far you agree with something.

1 ....

2 ....

3 ....

Need more practice?

On separate piece of paper, plan and write your response to the exam-style question below.

Exam-style question

'Elizabeth I was never in any real danger from the plots against her.'
How far do you agree?

You may use the following in your answer:

- Francis Walsingham
- Spain.

You **must** also use information of your own. **(16 marks)**

How confident do you feel about each of these **skills**? Colour in the bars.

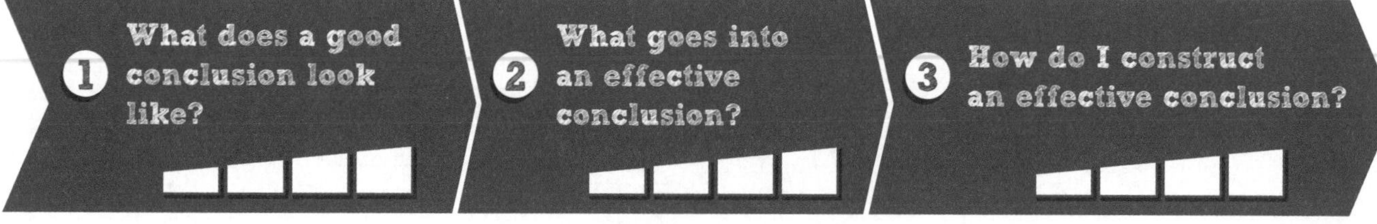
1 What does a good conclusion look like?
2 What goes into an effective conclusion?
3 How do I construct an effective conclusion?

Answers

Unit 1

Page 2

1 a to c ~~Elizabeth I became queen of England in 1558 after the death of her sister, Mary I. As Mary I had had no children, Elizabeth was next in line although she was a woman.~~ One key feature of the problems Elizabeth I faced on becoming queen was her gender. In Elizabethan society it was usual for men to be in positions of authority and she was only England's second queen. ~~Mary is sometimes known as 'Bloody Mary' because she burned over 300 Protestants~~.

2 a Suggestions include A, D and E to show legitimacy as a problem; B, C and F to show Mary Queen of Scots / France as a problem.

b The answer depends upon what was chosen for 2 a.

Page 3

1 Hierarchy or hierarchical

2 **Social hierarchy of the countryside:** Gentry; Yeomen; Landless, labouring poor.

Social hierarchy of towns: Merchants; Business owners; Skilled craftsmen.

3 A = c, i; B = a, h; C = b, d; D = f; E = e, d, g, j

4 Answers might include: calling and dismissing parliament; declaring war and peace; rule on some legal cases, where the law was unclear or if someone appealed a judgement; patronage (granting land, titles, money)

Page 4

5 A = a, g; B = answers might include b, d, e, h; C = b; D = c; E = a, f; F = b, h

6 a = false; b = true; c = false; d = true; e = false – no such title: he was Secretary of State; f = true; g = true; h = true

7 a i, ii, iii and iv; b i and iii; c i, ii, iii and iv

Page 5

1 A, B and E.

2 Answers could include: increased poverty; Catholic plots; the threat posed by Mary, Queen of Scots.

Page 6

1 B, D and E

2 a Answers could include: B and E because they provide supporting detail to show that Philip II wanted to get rid of Elizabeth I.

b Student's own answer.

Page 7

1 a to c One key feature of Elizabethan society was that it was a hierarchy. Your place in it depended on how much land you had and how wealthy you were. For example, in the countryside, the nobility were at the top of society and vagrants were at the bottom.

2 It will depend upon what the student has chosen.

Page 8

1

Think about …	Partly	Yes	No
Does the response answer the question?	✓		
Is there any description that doesn't show a key feature of the monarch in Elizabethan England?		✓	
Is the supporting evidence strong? Is it precise and relevant?	✓		

2 Elizabeth I was 25 when she came to the throne. It was thought unnatural for a woman to have authority. One important feature was that, as queen, she could rule in some legal cases such as when people appealed directly to her or the law was unclear. Not everyone agreed that Elizabeth should be queen as not everyone believed that Henry VIII could divorce Catherine of Aragon to marry Anne Boleyn. As queen, Elizabeth had a lot of power because monarchs in those days made all the important decisions.

3 Answers might include: declaring war, making peace, calling and dismissing parliament, making all important policy decisions.

Page 9

1 a, b This will depend upon what the student has decided to write about.

Unit 2

Page 12

1

	Points to make	Evidence
Intro	Religious settlement was Protestant but there was opposition from both Catholics and Protestants	
Section 1	Puritans – extreme Protestants, thought religious settlement – too Catholic. Didn't like Catholic look / feel of churches	Examples of Puritan beliefs, e.g. no bishops; no decoration; no miracle in mass
	Opposition sometimes very strong	Crucifix controversy – Elizabeth I backed down

Section 2	The Revolt of the Northern Earls 1569 opposed religious settlement; North of England Catholic	Catholic mass at Durham cathedral; third of nobles and lots of gentry in north = Catholic
	Rebellion aim = restore Catholic religion	Plot to put Mary, Queen of Scots on throne; she had strong claim so could be Catholic queen
	~~Earls angry and jealous of Elizabeth I's favourites~~	~~Robert Dudley, William Cecil~~
	~~Many Catholics opposed religious settlement because of the pope~~	~~Papal bull of excommunication 1570~~
Conclusion	Evidence shows opposition was from both Catholic and Protestants. Protestants thought the religious settlement too Catholic. Catholic opposition that led to the Northern Rebellion wanted Mary, Queen of Scots to become queen of England.	

2 Suggested answer: The vestments controversy – although the prompts are only prompts and do not have to be included. You would need to give more than one reason why Elizabeth I faced opposition however.

Page 13

1 (a) Protestant

(b) Catholic

2 Answers might include: she was Protestant; she was considered illegitimate by some as they did not accept that her father, Henry VIII, could divorce Catherine of Aragon and so was not really married to Anne Boleyn, her mother; there was a Catholic heir to the throne with no legitimacy questions (Mary, Queen of Scots).

3

Mostly Catholic	Mostly Protestant
Durham	London
Lancashire	Essex
Stafford	Kent

4 Answers might include: plain churches; plain tables instead of an altar; simple robes or ordinary clothes for priests; services and Bible in English; no 'miracle' / transubstantiation in mass; no pope; no / less hierarchy; no pilgrimages.

5 **Act of Supremacy:** made Elizabeth I supreme governor of the Church of England; all clergy to swear oath of allegiance to the queen.

Act of Uniformity: established appearance of churches and form of service held.

Royal Injunctions: A set of instructions on a range of issues, including how to enforce the Acts of Supremacy and Uniformity and on how people should worship God. Made it so all clergy were to teach the royal supremacy; each parish to have Bible in English; no preaching without a licence; pilgrimages to fake miracles banned; special vestments for clergy; anyone refusing to attend church to be reported to the Privy Council.

6 A fine of 1 shilling.

Page 14

7 (a), (c), (d)

8 A = c B = a C = b D = d

9 (a) = true; (b) = true; (c) = false – it was up to 400; (d) = false – every three to four years; (e) = true

10 (a) = C; (b) = V; (c) = C + V; (d) = C

11 Answers might include:

Causes of the rebellion: Religion; they were Catholics against the Elizabethan Religious Settlement; rebels disliked Elizabeth I's court favourites; they lost influence at court; rebels were ancient noble families who had lost influence in the north; some wanted to make Mary, Queen of Scots Elizabeth's heir.

Outcome / consequences of the rebellion: Rebels lost; Duke of Norfolk imprisoned; Earls of Northumberland and Westmorland fled; hundreds (450) of rebels executed; Mary, Queen of Scots moved to a castle further south; treason laws became harsher; a Protestant, the Earl of Huntingdon, put in charge of the Council of the North – and treated Catholics more harshly; power of the rebel families in the north was ended.

Page 15

1 A = c; B = b; C = a

2 (a) Describe **two** features of the monarchy in Elizabethan England.

(b) Explain why Elizabeth I faced opposition to her religious settlement in the years 1558–1569.

You may use the following in your answer:

- The vestments controversy
- The Revolt of the Northern Earls.

You **must** also include information of your own.

(c) 'The Elizabethan religious settlement largely resolved religious tensions in England.'
How far do you agree? Explain your answer.
You may use the following in your answer:

- the crucifix controversy
- the Revolt of the Northern Earls, 1569.

You **must** also include information of your own.

(16 marks)

Page 16

1. a, d, f, h
2. a i and iii

   b Because the question requires you to write about events only as far as 1569.

Page 17

1.

Which paragraph ...	Paragraph 1	Paragraph 2
includes relevant information about opposition?	✓	✓
develops an explanation of why there was opposition?	✓	Not developed

2. There isn't anything on the vestments controversy (it's not necessary to cover the prompts in the question, but it is a good idea to do so); and there isn't good explanation all the way through.

Page 18

1. Elizabeth I was able to enforce her religious settlement because it gave the Church of England powers to make sure that the clergy were obeying it. Visitations were a good way of doing this. A visitation was an inspection and the first ones were in 1559. Some ended up with ornaments in churches being destroyed because they were thought to be too Catholic. This angered Elizabeth I. She liked crucifixes, for example, although when puritans disagreed she had to back down on having them in all the churches. Visitations also included making sure that the clergy had licences to preach. This helped Elizabeth I to enforce the religious settlement because anyone who wanted a licence had to preach her religious settlement. For example, they preached the royal supremacy.

   The Act of Supremacy was a way of enforcing the religious settlement because it said that everyone had to take an oath to Elizabeth I as leader of the Church of England.

   Another way of enforcing the religious settlement was when Matthew Parker dealt with the vestments controversy. This is because he made it very clear what priests were expected to wear and those who refused lost their positions. This was another reason why Elizabeth I could enforce her religious settlement: priests who disobeyed knew they would lose their jobs.

2. One possible answer:

   a there is some specific evidence, used to make strong and relevant points.

   b there is a lot of irrelevant detail / filler / description. This wastes time, which is limited in an exam.

Unit 3

Page 22

1, 2 The answers will depend to an extent upon the student's point of view but evidence likely to lead them to side on disagrees more than agrees.

Page 23

1. a True; b False – literacy rates only rose from 20 to 30% for males; c False – they believed in it strongly; d False – they had tutors at home, like their brothers; e True – girls went to dame schools if they went to school at all (occasionally boys might); f False – they didn't get paid at all, they paid to be apprentices

2.

School	Who?	What did they learn?
No school	Most Elizabethan children, especially of labouring and landless poor	What they needed to know for the lives they would lead, learned from their family, e.g. cooking and brewing (girls) or looking after crops (boys)
Private tutors	Noble children, both girls and boys	Latin, Greek, history, philosophy, theology, government, foreign languages and the necessary skills (music, dancing, horse riding, archery). Boys also learned fencing, swimming, wrestling
Dame schools	Middle-class girls whose parents were able and willing to pay the small fees	Basic education – the 3 Rs (reading, writing, arithmetic), plus domestic skills
Petty schools	Middle-class boys; boys before they were old enough for grammar schools	Basic education – the 3 Rs (reading, writing, arithmetic)
Grammar schools	Boys from the professional classes, merchants' sons, very bright poor boys	Latin, Greek, religion, classical historians and philosophers; some sports. There were alternative, more practical curriculums for sons of merchants and craftsmen, including arithmetic, geography
Apprenticeships	Middle-class boys who wanted to learn a trade, sons of craftsmen and yeomen	Whatever was necessary to follow their chosen skill or profession – e.g. tailoring, metal working, printing, carpentry
University	Middle-class boys who wanted to enter a profession, e.g. law; noble boys	Geometry, music, astronomy, philosophy, logic and rhetoric as well as medicine, law and divinity; doctorates in medicine, law and divinity

Page 24

3

	Upper-class Female	Upper-class Male	Working-class Female	Working-class Male
Hunting on horseback with hounds	✓	✓		
Real tennis		✓		
Football				✓
Cock-fighting	✓	✓	✓	✓
Theatre	✓	✓	✓	✓
Listening to music at home	✓	✓		
Dancing	✓	✓	✓	✓

4 a False; b False; c True; d False; e True; f True; g False – quite the opposite; h True

5 A = d; B = a; C = b; D = c

6 New plays needed new, secular (non-religious) music to accompany them.

Page 25

1 B For example: only wealthier boys could go to grammar schools.
C For example: 10% for males and no improvement for females.
D For example: only 2 universities in England.

2 Student's own response. The evidence is likely to be classed as slightly or quite strong.

3 Likely to disagree that strong progress was made – 'strong' is a key word here.

Page 26

1 It will depend upon student's point of view. Theatre likely to be 'not violent' and the other two likely to be violent, though to what extent again depends.

2 Again – this will depend upon the student's point of view.

3 Again – this will depend upon the student's point of view.

Page 27

1

	Yes?	No?	Sometimes. It depended on ...
Plays	✓		
Music	✓		
Books			Plays were printed and read.

2 Students could use 'On the one hand' or 'it is true that' for the first gap and 'but on the other' or 'it is also true' on the second.

3 Answers will vary.

Page 28

1 Much Elizabethan entertainment was violent. Baiting, for example, was very popular and most towns had a bull ring where dogs were set upon a chained bull. Cockfighting was also enjoyed by Elizabethans, even Queen Elizabeth, as was bear baiting. When football was played there were no rules and players could even be killed. On the other hand, real tennis became popular too, although only rich men would play.

Other popular sports included hunting and wrestling, which could both be said to be violent. It is also true, however, that literature became increasingly popular in Elizabethan England so not all entertainment was violent. Accounts of voyages of discovery were in demand and most well-educated people wrote poetry. These things were only possible for the wealthy. Theatre, on the other hand, was available to everyone as even poor people could pay 1d to stand and watch a play. Sometimes there were queues of 2,000 people. As there were so many new plays written, and new music composed to go with them, it cannot be true to say that entertainment continued to be very violent as some changes show less violent pastimes were becoming more popular.'

Unit 4

Page 32

1
1 Mary, Queen of Scots. → England 1568
2 Northern Rebellion – Duke Of Norfolk to marry Mary, Queen of Scots 1569
Mary, Queen of Scots. = Catholic + claim to throne is strong
3 Papal excommunication → Catholics a threat; Mary, Queen of Scots = Catholic rival, strong claim to throne 1570
4 Ridolfi plot – Duke of Norfolk to depose Elizabeth I, marry Mary, Queen of Scots so Catholic queen 1571
5 Catholic priests start arriving in England 1574 – Mary, Queen of Scots greater threat?
6 Throckmorton plot – put Mary, Queen of Scots on throne; French and Spanish backing 1583
7 1585 threat to Elizabeth I worse – Elizabeth supported Dutch against Spain; France + Spain = allies
8 Babington plot 1586 wanted to put Mary, Queen of Scots on throne again; Mary, Queen of Scots is in on the plot!
9 1587 Mary, Queen of Scots executed after rumours Spanish landing in Wales

2 Likely answer(s): You might run out of time before you have covered the timespan in the question AND it could turn into a narrative of events.

Page 33

1

7 Babington plot Date: 1586	4 Ridolfi plot Date: 1571	9 The Spanish Armada Date: 1588
3 Papal bull of excommunication Date: 1570	1 Mary, Queen of Scots came to England Date: 1568	5 Catholic priests began arriving in England Date: 1574
2 Northern Rebellion Date: 1569	8 Execution of Mary, Queen of Scots Date: 1587	6 Throckmorton plot Date: 1583

2 a False; Mary, Queen of Scots was Henry VII's great granddaughter; b False; she was very reluctant to; c True; d True

3 A = e; B = b; C = a; D = d; E = c

Page 34

4 Answers might include: she had a strong claim to the throne; she was supported by Spain and the Guise family in France; she was Catholic; she was the focus of many plots against Elizabeth I.

5

Ridolfi 1571	Throckmorton 1583	Babington 1586
A, C, G	E, G	B, D, F, G

6 The evidence collected by Walsingham secured Mary, Queen of Scots' trial and conviction under the Act, which said that action could be taken against her once her role in the plot had been investigated. It was and her role in the plot led to her execution.

7 Walsingham had spies in every country in England and over 30 towns abroad. He also paid ordinary people for information so many spied on their neighbours. Other methods he used included torture/ciphers or ciphers/torture. Even the nobility were under suspicion.

Not all Catholic priests were executed and a special prison was built to keep them in. John Hart was a Catholic priest who spied for Walsingham in return for a pardon. However, 130 priests and 60 of their supporters were executed.

Page 35

1

Spanish threats	Plots
2 1587: Mary, Queen of Scots executed Elizabeth I reluctant but rumours Spanish troops had landed in January 1587	1 Papal bull: Catholics not to obey Elizabeth I. To overthrow Elizabeth I = good → Mary, Queen of Scots → queen
3 Babington timing – Spain threatening England	4 Other plots: Mary, Queen of Scots → Queen Throckmorton 1583
5 Spain threatened England 1587 – relations bad, worse 1585; Armada planned, aim = overthrow Elizabeth I; if Mary, Queen of Scots. alive she → queen	3 Babington 1586 aim = Mary, Queen of Scotts → throne

Page 36

1 **Point:** Babington plot shows that Mary, Queen of Scots was a danger, because she continued to be a focus of Catholic conspiracies against Elizabeth. This time, there was also proof that Mary herself wanted Elizabeth's death.

Explanation: Despite the failure of other plots, such as the Ridolfi plot in 1571 and the Throckmorton plot in 1583, and the execution of the plotters, the Babington plot showed that Mary was still the focus of Catholic plans to dethrone Elizabeth. It also showed that Mary, Queen of Scots actively encouraged these plots.

Evidence: Once again, Spain and France, Elizabeth's foreign enemies were both involved in the plot. Walsingham was able to intercept messages between Mary and Babington showing that Mary herself was one of the plotters.

Link back: Babington plot showed that Mary, Queen of Scots was not just the continued focus of Catholic plots to kill and/or replace Elizabeth, but that Mary herself was colluding with Spain and France to kill Elizabeth.

Page 37

1 a to c Another reason why Mary, Queen of Scots was a danger to Elizabeth I was the threat from Spain. It was very serious by 1584 when the Treaty of Joinville was signed, uniting France and Spain against Protestantism. By 1586, when the Babington plot to put Mary on the throne with Spanish and French support was uncovered, England was fighting Spain in the Netherlands and Drake was attacking Spanish colonies in the New World. This led Philip to decide to invade England. Although Mary was dead by the time of the Armada, her execution gave Spain another excuse to attack. So Spain made Mary, Queen of Scots a threat to Elizabeth I because …

c ii

2 a Although Mary, Queen of Scots was a great danger to Elizabeth I, Spain could be said to be more important. It supported Mary, Queen of Scots in numerous plots, which made them more serious because Spain was very wealthy and, from 1584, allied with France against Protestantism. The greatest threat faced by Elizabeth I, the Armada, was launched by Spain. …

b Student's own answer.

Page 38

1 Mary, Queen of Scots was executed in 1587 because of the Babington plot to put her on the throne instead of Elizabeth I. Mary, Queen of Scots had been in England since 1568 and had a strong claim to the English throne, which is a political reason she was dangerous. And the 1570 papal bull of excommunication said that Catholics ought to depose Elizabeth I, which shows religious reasons were important too. There were other plots like Ridolfi and Throckmorton too. Babington was serious because the Duke of Guise planned to invade England with 60,000 troops. Six Catholics were prepared to kill Elizabeth. When the Babington plot was made, England was under threat from Spain. The Ridolfi plot had come soon after the papal bull and was to make Mary queen of England. Philip II supported this plot. After Babington and before Mary was executed there were rumours that Spanish troops had landed in Wales. Mary was dangerous because she could take Elizabeth I's throne and she had support from Catholics at home and abroad.

Francis Walsingham was an important reason why Mary was executed. He intercepted letters between Babington and Mary, Queen of Scots and the Privy Council tried and convicted her of planning to assassinate Elizabeth I. Walsingham also uncovered the Throckmorton plot.

2

Skill	Paragraph 1	Paragraph 2
Make a clear point at the start of the paragraph.	✓	✓
Clearly explained how the reason given answers the question.	✓	
Provided supporting evidence.	✓	✓
Organised the information in the paragraphs into a logical order.	✓	
Linked back to the question at the end of the paragraph.	✓	

3. Link back to the question at the end of the paragraph.

Organise argument better: the papal bull and other plots against Elizabeth would be better dealt with in separate paragraphs before the Babington plot.

Explain more about Walsingham's role – his job.

Be clear about what kind of reasons Walsingham's role shows: political, religious, foreign policy.

Unit 5

Page 42

1. Possible answers might include that it jumps from one cause to another and then back again – there is no logical structure, making the answer harder to follow; Alba's army in the Netherlands is an important factor but might not make it into the essay in time.

2. Elizabeth I encouraged France against Spain: Alençon

Elizabeth I's support for Dutch to resist the Spanish, e.g. the Pacification of Ghent, 1576 and support for John Casimir, 1578

Spain supported Mary, Queen of Scots 1569 and 1571

In 1572 Drake raided Spanish ships taking £40,000

England = Protestants; Spain = Catholic

Drake raided Spain's New World colonies

Alba's army in Netherlands 1567

Drake took £400,000 from Spanish during circumnavigation

3. This answer will depend upon the student's point of view.

Page 43

1. A = e; B = a; C = b; D = c; E = d

2. a ii, iv b i, ii, iv

3. a = False b = True c = True – but it was also about interference in the government of the Netherlands d = True e = True

4. Spain's forces in the Netherlands going months without pay because Spain was almost bankrupt.

Page 44

5. It united all Dutch provinces, Catholic and Protestant; together they drew up the Pacification of Ghent.

6. b The Netherlands were to be completely independent from Spain – 'completely' is the key word.

7. a = 1578; b = 1579; c = 1578; d = 1579; e = 1579

8. To intervene directly in the Netherlands.

9.

The Pacification of Ghent Date: 1576 Event order: 2	Alençon withdrew from the Netherlands Date: 1579 Event order: 7	The Duke of Parma began making strong progress in the Netherlands Date: 1579 Event order: 6
	The Spanish Fury Date: 1576 Event order: 1	
Elizabeth I sent mercenaries to the Netherlands Date: 1577 Event order: 3	The Dutch Protestants asked Alençon for help Date: 1578 Event order: 5	Catholic provinces made peace with Spain Date: 1577 Event order: 4

Page 45

1, 2 a

a *The English conserved cannonballs for the decisive battle*	*b* *Elizabeth I let her commanders make naval decisions*	*c* *English galleons were faster and more mobile*
d *Poor communication between Sidonia's and Parma's fleets*	*e* *It took Parma 48 hours to prepare his ships*	*f* *The English stopped Medina Sidonia anchoring off the Isle of Wight*
g *English cannons and gun decks were better designed*	*h* *Spanish ships had poor quality cannonballs and supplies*	*i* *English ships could fire six times more cannonballs than Spanish*
j *English fireships created havoc*	*k* *Parma had lots of small ships*	*l* *Storms scattered the Armada*
m ~~*Philip II had received support from the Pope*~~	*n* *There were delays of 10 weeks before the Spanish ships set sail*	*o* *Two Spanish ships were captured off Plymouth*

b Note that statements c, g and i were issues of design though were not tactics. however, they did make other tactics possible.

3. a and b This answer will depend upon the student's point of view.

Page 46

1.

Netherlands 1567–1580		Drake 1567–1580	
England gave support to Dutch rebels. Many were Protestant. Philip II wanted to stamp out Protestantism and the rebellion. Elizabeth I was concerned at having a large Catholic army nearby. Philip II was prepared to use it in the Ridolfi plot.	R	Drake traded illegally with Spain's New World colonies and raided Spanish ships and settlements. Elizabeth I backed him. Drake made them both a lot of money. He sailed around the globe and claimed a region of North America for England.	E

2. **Political:** A, B, C, F, also E, D (attacks on Spain); **Religious:** A, C; **Economic:** D, E, F

Page 47

1. a

Extract A

In 1567 Anglo–Spanish relations declined because Spain sent Alba to the Netherlands with a large army to stamp out heresy (Protestantism), which also threatened England's security. This is religious and political. Soon after, in 1569 and 1571, Catholic plots against Elizabeth I were developed that included Alba's army in their plans to support England's Catholics. This means it was religious. However, it was also political.

Extract B

Politics and religion often combined to cause a decline in Anglo–Spanish relations. In 1567, Spain sent Alba's army to the Netherlands to stamp out heresy (Protestantism), which threatened England's security. The threat grew in 1569 and 1571 when there were Catholic plots to overthrow Elizabeth I involving Alba's army. These events in the decline in Anglo–Spanish relations were both political and religious because they involved the overthrow of Elizabeth I to replace her with a Catholic monarch.

b Extract B is stronger because it describes how religion and politics combined.

2. Likely to vary greatly student to student.

Page 48

1.

Skill	Weak		Strong	
Explanation	Narrative with some examples	✓	Explains reasons for decline	
Evidence	Vague, imprecise, not very accurate		Accurate, specific and precise	✓
Organisation	None: hard to follow		Yes: chronological or by theme	
Analysis	A list of reasons with 'economic' or 'political' added on	✓	Organised according to political and economic causes	

2. Answers might include organising by theme rather than chronologically; trying to avoid a list of reasons – develop explanations further.

Page 49

1.

	A	B	C	D	E	F
Political	✓	✓	✓	✓	✓	✓
Economic	✓	✓			✓	
Religious	✓		✓			✓

2. Answers will vary according to students' interpretations of the evidence, but politics comes out as most important; some students might give religion more importance based on deeper knowledge of the evidence given.

Unit 6

Page 52

1. b, c, f, g, i, j
2. a, c (Throckmorton), d, e, h
3. Answers will vary.

Page 53

1. d deposing King Philip II of Spain.

2.

William of Orange	Duke of Alençon
A C E H	B C D F G

3.

1580	Throckmorton plot
1581	Treaty of Nonsuch; Leicester sent to the Netherlands with troops to support the Dutch Protestant rebels; Drake raided Spain's New World colonies
1583	Spain acquired Portugal
1584	Deaths of Duke of Alençon and William of Orange. Treaty of Joinville
1585	Spain launched the Armada – it was defeated
1586	Alençon visited England; Elizabeth I gave him £70,000
1587	Babington plot; Leicester accepted title of Governor General of the Netherlands for Elizabeth I
1588	Drake's raid on Cadiz; Leicester returned to England for good after not a very successful campaign

Page 54

4. a False – it was the singeing of the King of Spain's beard.

   b False – it was the other way round.

   c True

   d False – the Treaty of Joinville in 1584 effectively ended any alliance.

   e False – there were some small successes, including depriving Parma's fleet of a deep water port; this proved helpful against the Armada.

   f False – he had definitely made it by the end of 1585.

5. a Duke of Alba. He is Catholic; all the others are Protestant; alternatively, all the others supported the Netherlands against Spain. The answer could also be John Casimir. He was a mercenary, the others were 'official' military leaders.

   b Duke of Alençon. He was French and all the others were Spanish; alternatively, all the others supported Spain against the Netherlands.

c Portugal. All the others were Spanish territories in the New World. They were all Spanish possessions after 1580.

d The launch of the Armada. All the other events happened in 1587.

e William Stanley. He defected to the Spanish.

6 A = d; B = e; C = b; D = a; E = c

Page 55

1 **Short-term:** D, E, G, H, I, J

Long-term: A, B, C, D, E, F

2 Answers will vary although it is now thought that Drake's raids on Spanish New World colonies under orders from Elizabeth I finally persuaded Philip II to prepare the Armada.

Page 56

1 **Long-term cause: English intervention in Dutch Revolt** = I

Long-term cause: religious rivalry = D, E, G

Long-term cause: New World = H, J

2 Answers will vary.

Page 57

1 a Extract A is narrative.

b Philip II decided to invade England in 1585 after Drake's raid on Spanish new World colonies. This, on top of all his other raids (e.g. 1572, 1577–1580) greatly worsened long-term Anglo–Spanish relations. Philip II's decision coincided with Elizabeth I helping Dutch rebels under the Treaty of Nonsuch. The Netherlands was a long-term problem but by 1585 Spain had Portugal's resources and had made an alliance with France in 1584. All these factors combined to make Philip prepare an Armada.

2 By 1585, Anglo-Spanish relations had been in D decline. In the G / H this decline was E by Elizabeth I's support for Francis Drake's attacks on Spanish colonies (e.g. 1577–1580 and 1585). A / C / F the 1585 Treaty of Nonsuch, when England agreed to support Dutch rebels, Philip II decided to act against Elizabeth. A / C / F improved relations with France under the Treaty of Joinville in 1584, and A / C / F Spain's wealth increasing after it got Portugal in 1580, G / H factors B the long to convince Philip to build the Armada against England.

Page 58

1 Answers will vary.

2 Rebellion in the Netherlands = h, c, f

Drake = b, i, e, a

Religion = h, j, c, f, g (Throckmorton, Babington), a

Unit 7

Page 62

1 Most could be used for both. This answer is not necessarily the only correct combination.

Question 1	Both Questions	Question 1
A, B, C, D, E, H, I	A, B, C, D, I	A, B, C, D, F, G, I

2 Answers will vary.

Page 63

1 a i

b ii

c iv

d i, ii, iii, iv

2 a A = f B = b C = c D = a E = d F = e G = g

b

	Drake	Hawkins	Raleigh
Voyages	B, C, D	A, B	E, F, G

Page 64

3 a False – Elizabeth I would not let him.

b False – they did not collaborate; the upper classes were not prepared to work.

c True

d True – because the *Tiger* had run aground.

e False – they returned to England and acted as translators and go-betweens. Manteo led the settlers in 1587.

f True

g False – they thought that the Algonquians would work for them and they would rule over them.

4 Answers might include: they were women as well as men; they had come from poor parts of London and would be used to hardship.

5 1585–1586 = Ralph Lane 1587–1590 = Manteo (Grenville and White led the expeditions)

6 J = 1 F = 2 E = 3 D = 4
B = 5 L = 6 G = 7 A = 8
H = 9 I = 10 C = 11 K = 12

A comes before H as these roles were allocated by Raleigh before the colonists left.

Page 65

1 a Answers will vary, but probably Drake.

b Answers will vary.

c Answers will vary.

2 a Answers will vary, but probably Raleigh.

b Answers will vary.

c Answers will vary.

Page 66

1 a

A	The colonists left England too late to plant crops to harvest for the winter.
B	Vital supplies of seeds, food and gunpowder were lost when the *Tiger* ran aground.
C	The colonists did not have the right mix of skills to tackle the challenges of a new colony.
D	The English were dependent on the Native Americans for help and food.
E	Although welcoming at first, the Native Americans turned against the English.
F	Chief Wingina, who ruled the region, was unpredictable and did not trust the colonists.
G	The English brought diseases that killed many Algonquians, turning them against the colonists.

b Answers will vary, but F links to E and possibly G and D too.

2 Answers will vary.

3 a and b Answers will vary.

Page 67

1 A = short, B = long, C = long, D = long, E = long, F = long/short, G = short, H = long, I = short, J = long

2 a and b Possibly A, D which link to E. Possibly B, C, D, G, J.

3 Answers will vary.

4 Answers will vary.

Page 68

1 a Native American resistance: D, E, F, G

The colonists: A, C, D, H, possibly F to an extent

Poor planning: A, C

Luck: B, E, G (disease not understood), possibly F (colonists had no control over this reason)

b Here is one possible answer.

A The colonists left England too late to plant crops to harvest for the winter (voyage).

B Vital supplies of seeds, food and gunpowder were lost when the *Tiger* ran aground (voyage).

The colonists did not have the right mix of skills.

The English were very dependent on the Native Americans for help and food to survive.

Wingina believed the English had supernatural powers from their god to use against the Native Americans.

Wingina, who ruled the region, was unpredictable and did not trust the colonists.

The English brought diseases that killed many Algonquians, turning them against the colonists.

Lane led an attack against the Algonquians after discovering Wingina planned to ambush them.

2 Responses will vary.

3 Responses will vary.

Page 69

1 a 1584: Raleigh sent a fact-finding expedition to Virginia.

b This was the first expedition to establish a colony and so no one had any previous experience.

c The expedition leader, Grenville, and governor of Virginia, Lane, did not get on.

d The colonists left England too late to plant crops to harvest for the winter.

e Vital supplies of seeds, food and gunpowder were lost when the *Tiger* ran aground.

f The colonists did not have the right mix of skills and were not used to hardship.

g The colonists were very dependent on the Native Americans for help and food to survive.

h Wingina, who ruled the region, was unpredictable and did not trust the colonists.

i The English brought diseases that killed many Algonquians, turning them against the colonists.

j The colonists twice led attacks against the Native Americans, in 1586 and 1587.

Other variations on the answer are possible.

3 Answers will vary, but the colonists is a likely answer, or possibly inexperience.

4 Answers will vary.

Unit 8

Page 72

1

Conclusion checklist	✓
Gives overall summary of the key points of the essay	✓
Gives a clear, supported judgement	
Answers the question directly – uses question wording	✓
No surprises – doesn't suddenly bring in any new information	

2 Answers will vary – but overall it is (very) effective.

Page 73

1

	more likely	less likely
households headed by working, adult males		✓
households headed by working, adult females	✓	
those younger than 16 years old	✓	
16–60-year-olds		✓
those over 60 years old	✓	
people with disabilities or illnesses	✓	
skilled workers		✓

2 Sheep farming became profitable → b → c → d → a → There was an increase in vagrancy.

3 d

4 Common land was land that everyone could use. It helped poor people by providing foraging, firewood and could also be used for grazing animals (pigs usually).

Page 74

5. The poor rate was the money collected. It was given out to the poor as poor relief.
6. a = True

   b = True

   c = False – quite the opposite.

   d = True – Vagrants could be imprisoned, whipped or even executed.

   e = False – They were the first to recognise unemployment as a genuine problem.

   f = True

   g = True – Arresting them cost the tax payers more money.
7. 1563 Statute of Artificers = d

   1572 Vagabonds Act = a, c, e, f

   1576 Poor Relief Act = b
8. D = a E = b A = c B = d C = e

Page 75

1. a

Does the conclusion …	Student A	Student B
answer the question directly, using the question wording?	✓	✓
give an overall summary of the key points of the essay?	✓	✓
give a clear judgement about how far sheep farming was the most important reason for poverty?	✓	✓
provide supporting information for its key points?		✓

   b The most important reason for poverty in Elizabethan England was population growth, which was up to 35%. This forced up prices for everything, including food and rent. Sheep farming became more profitable because of population growth and there was some enclosure, which caused poverty, but only 2–3% of land was affected. Unemployment, on the other hand, was a much bigger problem as is shown by it being recognised for the first time in the Vagabonds Act of 1572. For these reasons, sheep farming was not the most important reason for poverty in Elizabethan England. Although it played a part, unemployment was more important, and population growth was the most important reason of all.

   c Its use of supporting information to back up its conclusion.

2. It will vary, so these are suggestions:

   Overall population growth was **the most important** reason for poverty in Elizabethan England. **Furthermore**, sheep farming was **not as important a factor** because only 2–3% of land was enclosed. Also unemployment was **perhaps more important** than sheep farming too, because it was included in the 1572 Vagabonds Act. **In conclusion**, population growth was most important because it contributed to all the other causes.

Page 76

1. Answers will vary but ought to begin / say something like either …

   "Overall unemployment was not the most important cause of poverty in Elizabethan England …"

   OR "In conclusion, population growth was more important than unemployment as a cause of …"
2. a C

   b B and D

   c Perhaps more important than unemployment, however, was population growth.

   d A
3. Answers will vary but ought to be similar to examples given above.

Page 77

1. Answers will vary according to which cause the student thinks was most important and the relative importance of other causes. It ought to follow the structures show above.

Page 78

1. There is a direct opening sentence; there is a couple of sentences that explain their most important reason for vagabondage. Brief comments on other factors.
2. Enclosure has not been mentioned; there is nothing that says how far enclosure was to blame for vagabondage compared.
3. Answers will vary but could include that the student should use the question wording and briefly set out their answer in one or two sentences.

Page 79

1. Answers will vary.

Notes